"Are You Happy With That?"

At the Solicitor's in Swansea

"I'm a

… …

Are you ne…

No, I'm sorry, 'I'm afraid' does not m   that I am afraid. There is nothing to fear.

… …

Are you happy with that?

All communications and letters will be in English.

… …

Are you happy with that?

No, I'm not asking you how you feel. 'Are you happy with that?' simply means, 'Now, can we proceed?' And that is not a question.

… …

Are you happy with that?

The Adjudicator has refused refugee status for you.

… …

Are you happy with that?

You are to be evicted from your accommodation and you face deportation.

… …

Are you happy with that?

Now, this paragraph is you, sign here, and here, thank you. You will hear from me shortly, you need not do anything, just leave it all to me.

… …

Are you happy with that?"

Sylvie Hoffmann)

ARE YOU
HAPPY
WITH THAT?

Hafan Books
Tenth Anniversary Collection

by

People Seeking Sanctuary
in Wales

Editor: Tom Cheesman

With thanks to the editors of previous anthologies – Eric Ngalle Charles, Grahame Davies, Latéfa Guémar, Sylvie Hoffmann and Jeni Williams – and to all who have helped others write and translate

Contact: t.cheesman@swansea.ac.uk

    or: Hafan Books, c/o Tom Cheesman

              Dept of Languages

              Swansea University

              SA2 8PP

All proceeds to Swansea Bay Asylum Seekers Support Group

ISBN: 978-0-9569473-76
Published in Swansea by Hafan Books, 2013
Printed by Lulu.com
Hafan Books are at: **www.lulu.com/hafan**

Are You Happy With That? is number 6 in the anthology series 'Refugees Writing in Wales'. Some contents first appeared in previous numbers:

Between a Mountain and a Sea (2003) ISBN 09545147-0X
Nobody's Perfect (2004) 978-0-9545147-16
Soft Touch (2005) 09545147-34
Gŵyl y Blaidd / Festival of the Wolf (2006, with Parthian) 978-1-9057622-00
Fragments from the Dark (2008) 978-0-9545147-47

Front cover image: detail of a painting © by Tarek Tuma: 'Portrait of Hamza Bakkour' (age 13, wounded by an army bullet, Hamza died two days later in Homs, Syria, in February 2012)

Back cover image: detail of a photomontage © by Humberto Gatica: from the 'Memory Tree' series. See Part 3.

Cover design by Mostyn Jones

Contents

In loving memory of good friends we lost along the way:

Ben Lockwood (1981–2005)

Beti Rhys (1901–2003)

Kalan Kawa Karim (1975–2004)

Lauraann Da Costa Grobler (1976–2004)

Richard 'Rej' Jones (1957–2011)

William Gamu Mbwembwe (1964–2008)

When the night has come and the land is dark
And the moon is the only light we'll see
No I won't be afraid – no I won't be afraid
Just as long as you stand by me

If the sky that we look upon should tumble and fall
Or the mountain should crumble to the sea
I won't cry – I won't cry – no I won't shed a tear
Just as long as you stand by me

Ben E. King, 1961

With special thanks to **Roger Warren-Evans**, Barrister (retired), of Mumbles, who created the charity **Asylum Justice** and ran it from 2007 to 2013, personally working much more than full time on the caseload. Asylum Justice provided crucial free legal advice and representation to many thousands of asylum seekers and refugees across South Wales. Thanks also to all the legal professionals and other volunteers who worked with Asylum Justice over these years.

Useful websites

Swansea

Swansea Bay Asylum Seekers Support Group:

swanseabassgroup.org

Swansea City of Sanctuary: **cityofsanctuary.org/swansea**

Share Tawe (*helping local people help destitute asylum seekers*):

sharetawe.org.uk

Wales

Displaced People in Action: **dpia.org.uk**

Wales Migration Partnership: **wsmp.org.uk**

Welsh Refugee Council: **welshrefugeecouncil.org.uk**

UK

Asylum Aid (*legal support*): **asylumaid.org.uk**

National Coalition of Anti-Deportation Campaigns
(*contact NCADC if someone you know is at risk of deportation*):

ncadc.org.uk

Detention Action: **detentionaction.org.uk**

Freedom from Torture (Medical Foundation):

freedomfromtorture.org

Medical Justice: **medicaljustice.org.uk**

Refugee Council: **refugeecouncil.org.uk**

Refugee Action: **refugee-action.org.uk**

Part 1

Ways in ...

Poems and stories by seekers of sanctuary and their friends

"Are You Happy With That?"

Alhaji Sheku Kamara

I heard two sanctuary seekers chatting
Chatting about their situation
Said the first one:
"Man I am sick and tired with this immigration reporting thing
Every week I have to report at the immigration
Damn I'm tired with this signing thing
Especially when it's raining
As from today I will not be reporting any more
If you were a UK Border Force officer
I would have asked you
Are you happy with that?"

The other responded:
"Man can't you see my situation? I've been made destitute
I don't even have a penny to spend and
On my friends I depend
I'm not even allowed to work
It will be illegal if I do
But I have no choice cos I have to live
So I'm gonna start working illegally anyway
And I will not give a damn – just as long as the money
I will be paying as tax
Will be used legally
And not to buy guns, bombs or to sponsor war
If you were a tax officer I would have asked you
Are you happy with that?

After this conversation
I will just leave this place and disappear
I know you will not be happy with that
So I will not ask
But if you were the Home Office
I would have asked you
Are you happy with that?"

<Alhaji Sheku Kamara came to the UK from west Africa as a young man, seeking sanctuary from civil wars in Sierra Leone and Liberia. From 2003 he became a key player and later captain of Swansea World Stars football team. For more of his poems, and more about him, see Part 3 of this book.

>Sliva Kiki is a Kurdish refugee from Damascus, Syria. She has been living in Swansea since 2009 with her two teenage sons. She studied law for two years in Syria. Sliva often acts as a volunteer interpreter for Arabic and Kurmanji, and she would like to gain qualifications so she can do more to help refugees in the UK, and those in Syria and neighbouring countries. Sliva's poem came out of workshops run by Jeni Williams (see page 62) at the Swansea Museum exhibition "Home From Home?" (created with Swansea City of Sanctuary) in 2012.

No Celebration This Year

(Damascus, August 2012)

Sliva Kiki

She says, no celebration this year.
She is five.
She is thinking about the children who go away
and don't come back.
She is thinking about the other children
the children hungry or in a safer place.
She says, no celebration this year.

She says, what will happen with us?
With other people.
With our neighbours.
With friends.
She is carefully thinking.

She is carefully thinking.
She says, no celebration this year.
She is thinking.

She asks her nani.
She wants to stay at her house.
Her own house is too much high.
She hears the tank sound and the plane sound.
She says, what will happen with us?

She says, what will happen with us?
She is waiting until everything is finished
before she goes outside with her friends to play
her favourite game.
She is carefully thinking.

She is carefully thinking.
When the evening comes
she says, what will happen with us?
She says, when the morning comes
can I go again outside?

That Girl

Mohadeseh Habibi

That girl running in the school yard
is so happy.
Everybody looks at her. She smiles all the time.
She loves to hear the birds singing.
I am with her and I can smell flowers.

Her clothes are a green field
scattered with the red flowers of spring.
Her loose hair ripples in the wind
like the weeping willow.

She has a sound quiet as the spring breeze.
The water drop on the flower after rain:
that is the freshness of her skin.
The blue of the sky:
that is the colour of her bright eye.

We are sixteen.
I am with her and I am free as air.

I would give one year of my life now
for one day with her again.

A Man and a Woman

Mohadeseh Habibi

In the picture I can see two people
They are everything in my life
I see a man with grey hair and a woman.

Her eyes are worried
The man's hands are worn
He has been working very hard.

I can see a woman who is always worried for her children
It is so long since she has seen them.
It is a long time.

We watch the screen hungrily
They get the picture and I get the sound

I want to touch them, hug them, kiss them
I don't like just to watch their picture
I want to look into their eyes and be with them.

I want to touch their skin, it is tired, so tired, and rough
I love them as much as I love myself
I don't know when I will ever see them.

This is a picture of my mother and father.

<**Mohadeseh Habibi** from Afghanistan wrote these poems in 2012 in the Swansea Museum workshops run by Jeni Williams. Jeni helped her translate them. Mohadeseh came to Swansea in 2008 with her husband. They have two young children. As happens to many refugees, different members of Mohadeseh's family have ended up in different countries. Most of them have been granted permission to stay, but they cannot yet be reunited in one place because they do not have the necessary travel documents. At the time of writing, her brother is in France, her mother in Sweden and her father in Germany. The grandparents have never seen little Maryam. The family just all want to be together.

>**Hannah Sabatia** from Kenya wrote the sequence "The Door Poems" in Jeni's workshops. Hannah is a qualified nutritionist and a single parent who, since coming to Swansea seeking sanctuary, has played a full and vibrant role in voluntary organizations in the city. A natural leader and community builder, a gifted public speaker, she is vice-chair of Swansea City of Sanctuary, active in the Swansea Advocacy Forum for asylum seekers and refugees, has gained an NVQ in Community Development, is working towards a PGCE in Adult Education, teaches English as a volunteer to parents at Hafod Primary School, at the African Community Centre and the Minority Ethnic Women's Network and at drop-ins run by the Cyrenians, and has made important contributions to the LEANA project (Local Education and Advice on Nutrition and Activity) run by Swansea Council for Voluntary Service.

Hannah hopes to be granted leave to remain and the right to work, in order to have a career in public health education in the UK.

At the time of writing, Hannah's asylum application has just been turned down at judicial review.

The Door Poems

Hannah Sabatia

(i)   and there he was

A door opens
        and there he was

Standing about ten yards away
he called her to come out
she did not dare

The child saw him
afraid too

He went away
they locked the door
never saw him again

(ii)   and he comes in with a mobile in his hand

A door opens
        and he comes in with a mobile in his hand
unsure

The wife is inside with the child

There is a quarrel

He has no self-control
he slaps her on the face
slaps her till she passes out
slaps her till she passes out
like dark night the room turns
she sees stars like in the heavens

But when she rises up
he is crying as usual
swearing never again

Never again

Never again

But only for this moment

(iii)   and she comes in running

A door opens
       and she comes in running

A beautiful young girl panting for breath
afraid of what has happened
it was a tense moment

Hurry up and hide, that's all I could say
her masters were fighting
on this fateful evening
the sun had already gone down

She had gone to open the gate
he was drunk, forced her in the car
he forced her but the wife saw them

She was the house-help
loyal and friendly
she did all her chores

(iv)   and we enter one by one

A door opens
       and we enter one by one

We are searched head to toe
as one by one we enter

We must remember all the details
all the details we want to forget
young
old
we sit on the cold long benches
wait and wait

Come in here
go in there
sit by here
stand by here
do you understand

All we need is safety
but

Why did you lie?
threats
threats

All we speak is taped
taped and recorded
one by one

(v)   and in comes the chef

A door opens
    and in comes the chef

Another day of boiled eggs for breakfast
a year feels like a decade
the routine and monotony of the hostel
waiting
and
waiting
nobody knowing when decisions will come

A long day and nothing new
out in the endless fields
long barbed spiked wire at the edge

The morning sun a warm blanket

We take photographs of our long shadows
they are metres long

A long day, a long, long day

Memories of nothing

(vi)   and suddenly, with great force,

A door opens
        and suddenly, with great force

they come in twos and fours
with padded chests, chains, sledgehammers, handcuffs
nikama jitu, hawajali, haja uondoke ...*
black uniforms, huge, faceless

She coils under the bed

Again under the sofa

In the cupboard

Then tries the shelves

But the baby cries uncontrollably

Nowhere to hide after all

Swahili: "Like a giant, they don't care, as long as you get out..."

(vii)   and the boy comes in

A door opens
     and the boy comes in

Panting, sweat runs down his face
he clings to his mother's dress
like he has met her for the first time

It's raining and cold

The mother calms him down
gives him a glass of warm milk

Slowly the boy speaks
all that his six years have seen

Excuse me can I play with you?
Excuse me can I play with you?
Excuse me…
can I …
  play
    with
      you?

No boy stops

School after school
the other bigger boys run after him
he is alone, doesn't recall their names
they all look alike, cool, flicking their fine hair off their faces

The boy fails to understand

Mum, what colour am I?

And there are other things he cannot say

>**Fridah Kimani** came to the UK in 2002 with her mother Lydia, fleeing ethnic violence in Kenya. Her poem "Through the Eyes of a Window" was written in Swansea in 2006 when she was 11. It won a UK-wide writing competition for young people and has been published in several places, including a national magazine for young carers, as well as in our collection *Fragments from the Dark* (2008). Fridah and Lydia are now UK citizens. Fridah did her A-levels in 2013 and is starting a degree in Early Childhood Studies.

Through the Eyes of a Window

Fridah Kimani

Take me, I'm a window.
I have lots of different feelings,
especially Lonely and Hated.

Lonely because no one looks or cleans me,
they just walk past and take no notice.

Hated because of my owners.
They have people chucking eggs and stones
and I take the hate not them.

What if I fall to pieces, my soul will be broken
and someone else will take my place

I know I'm hated and I feel lonely
but PLEASE don't BREAK my SOUL

OH NO! I can see a stone coming my way,
what shall I do?

This might be my last moment ...!

I Feel Like Nobody Here

Maxson Sahr Kpakio

Dedicated to asylum seekers and refugees in the UK

I feel like nobody here, ashamed, like everybody
Hates me,
But they don't know me, they really
Don't know who I am either,
Only they know what they read in the
Newspapers about me
And that is not me.

I feel like nobody here,
Despite the torture and persecution I managed
To escape from home, in search
Of a land of peace and respect for
Human rights – as soon as I got in,
I was put into detention centre,
And the newspapers did the rest.

I feel like nobody here,
People are being beat up and killed
Sometimes just because they are
Asylum seekers,
But please, could you find out better.

We didn't come here for this, we try to leave
Behind this, we try to find peace here, but it's
Far from being possible, not with this media.

They refer to me as bogus asylum seeker,
And they even told others that I am
Just a parasite, and a disease carrier,
But that is not me.

If it was good at home where respect for human
Rights and relative peace was like before,

I would go home tomorrow.
I didn't want to come here, I didn't want
To be a refugee either.
But I am here and I want to contribute
And fit in.
But how can I?
How can people really accept me when
All they read about me is rubbish,
Nothing but rubbish.

But I don't blame them for fear of me,
They believe
What
They read.

I feel like nobody here,
I want to meet them
And speak to them and tell them it's
Not true.
Let me tell them that I am
Not what they read in
The newspapers.

<Maxson Sahr Kpakio was born in Liberia. He was forced to flee political instability and civil war after witnessing the war for ten years. When he reached the UK he was 'dispersed' to Swansea by the Home Office. Soon after arriving he wrote a short drama, "It Could Happen To You Too", which was performed twice in 2002 by members of Swansea Bay Asylum Seekers Support Group. He has since volunteered and worked for many organizations including the Citizens Advice Bureau, Victim Support, British Red Cross, and Swansea Council for Voluntary Service. He also gained a BA in International Relations from Swansea University. Max is committed to helping others, here and back in Liberia too. He founded a voluntary organization, Wales-Liberia Connect, to combat HIV/AIDS in both countries. He recently got a job at the DVLA.

His poem "I Feel Like Nobody Here" is based on a record of discussions in the Refugee Link Group of the Wales Refugee Media Forum, convened by Displaced People in Action, in 2002-3. This 'found poem' had great impact after it appeared in *Between a Mountain and a Sea*. Max was often invited to perform it, a group at the Sherman Theatre (Cardiff) dramatised it, and it has been reprinted many times.

>Aliou Keita was born late in the rainy season in August 1977 in Masala, Republic of Mali. He grew up in a small farming village. He studied sociology and anthropology at the University of Bamako (the capital of Mali) before (as he put it in 2003) "the events that changed his life and eventually brought him to Swansea", seeking sanctuary. His poems (in French, translated by Sylvie Hoffmann) appeared in *Between a Mountain and a Sea* and *Nobody's Perfect*. After his case was rejected, he became homeless and suffered psychological illness. Aliou disappeared from Swansea in 2006. We would love to hear from him and just hope he has found somewhere safe.

Bird Without Tree

Aliou Keita

Orphan Bird flies in the sky
Where to live

Poor Bird looks for somewhere
His confused destination gives him the will
To live

Wounded Bird needs the Tree where to live
Somewhere

Every single bird tries hard to find the Highest Tree
To live
The Tree found between Mountain and Sea
Somewhere
Every single bird needs to be protected
Somewhere

Orphan Bird flies in the sky
Where to live

Poor Bird
Crowded by grumblings of unfriendly moods
In every place! In every sky! On every tree!
Where is the Bird supposed to live?

Wounded Bird
Oh! Innocent!
Rest! Rest! Keep Hope! Somewhere!

Two Stories

Andy Hyka

The Dragon in the Castle

Once upon a time there was a dragon and he was hungry for food and he didn't have anything. He flew out on the sky and he found a castle and he found some soldiers. He ate all the soldiers in the castle. Then he found some real food and it was chicken, bread and cheese and then he flew back to his house.

The Soldiers Killing the Good People

One hot day the king wanted to build his face with rocks and he didn't have anybody to build it. The soldiers said to the king: We will go and look for some people to build it for you. The soldiers found some good people and they started to build the king's face. The soldiers killed anybody who wasn't working. They saw a man resting on the ground and the soldiers killed him.

Sunday 11 March 2001

Andy Hyka

On that day in Macedonia the police were knocking everybody's door because   said a lie at the police   the police saying to everybody who was saying a lie and   somebody told a lie   and they said like it was us   they   he said search the house but it wasn't us   it was somebody else   so the police came and knocked and knocked our door and I ran into the house because I was playing in the front door with my Grompa but they got my Grompa and hit him and and they hanged him up.

< **Andy Hyka** from Macedonia was 8 and going to school in Newport when we published his "Two Stories" in 2003. The next year we published "Sunday March 2001". He had fled the violence of the nationalist conflicts in Macedonia and Albania, somehow reached the UK but without any family, and was taken into foster care. We have since lost touch with Andy and his foster family and hope he is well, wherever he is now.

> **William Gamu Mbwembwe** came from Harare, the capital of Zimbabwe, to the UK to seek sanctuary in 2004. He describes why he did so in the following story. He contributed the story to *Soft Touch* (2005), along with the powerful political poems which are also reprinted here.

The early 2000s was a time of often violent conflict in Zimbabwe between President Mugabe's supporters and opponents. Coupled with economic melt-down, the conflict led to about one quarter of the population (over 3 million people) leaving the country, mostly to South Africa. But Swansea was lucky enough to receive William and his family, who after reaching the UK claimed asylum and were randomly 'dispersed' by the Home Office to Wales. William Mbwembwe had a big impact here, even while he was still "living on NASS handouts" as he says in his story (NASS = the National Asylum Support Service, which has since been abolished). He placed his many talents in the service of the newly established African Community Centre (ACC), where he was very effective and popular as the first volunteer Manager, and he quickly became a highly respected person in the Swansea community. Shortly after being granted refugee status in 2008, William tragically died of a sudden illness, leaving a widow and two children.

From the South South to the North West

William G. Mbwembwe

I come from a land way down in the south – though it's a small country, it's bigger than the islands of Great Britain. This is where the winters are not as cold and the summer is just too hot. I mean damn, that place is hot. Sometimes the cold is good coz it keeps you moving, but when it's seething hot, all you wanna do is get some shade and snooze off.

I was born privileged but not very. We lived in a low density suburb for the upper middle class. I was a manager in a small company that made tons of cash money, I had my own house, my own car plus company car. So what the hell am I doing in this place living on NASS handouts?

Well …

It was a sunny Saturday afternoon and here we were. Anybody who was somebody met here on the weekend, some to show off their latest acquisitions, be it a new car or a new girl. This is kwaMereki in downtown Harare. We met here for a braai (bar-b-q), and Amai Gringo or any one of the ladies would make sadza (that's maize-corn mash, Shona-style). Even though the sadza looked suspect healthwise, it sure did taste better than the one the missus made at home. Some brought their families, which I felt was out of place, this was the big boys' play area. Even though beer was drunk outside, the police didn't bother anybody. As for plumbing – behind your car would be good enough, but of course for the serious stuff you'd have to go home.

Anyway, on this particular afternoon we were there as usual and music was blaring from the speaker on the door of one of the bottle stores and I still remember Eddy Grant's "Gimme Hope Jo'Anna" being played more than once. What irony coz on this day we were talking politics. This was April 2000 and the last six months had brought too many changes. The government felt threatened. A new political party had everybody singing its name, the government's draft constitution had been rejected by the people, and elections were just around the nearest corner. The government decided to go on the African type of offensive, beat everybody into submission. The main spy agency, the CIO, was working overtime. I didn't see the unmarked police car, I had gone to do the plumbing thing a few cars away, but I finished in time to see my "political analysis and debate team" being bundled into the car and I knew it would be wiser to head home.

Reports of people being tortured or killed were in the papers daily, man it was ugly, this was no scary movie this was for real, but of course it was happening elsewhere so I did not panic. But when the invaders invaded the farm across the road and started demanding food and water, I knew vamoosing was the best advice. We packed up all our stuff including the roaches (you don't leave those behind – they are family), and we headed off to live somewhere else (which I won't say coz I don't trust you).

The house I had left behind, in the months before and after the elections it was ransacked. Neighbours told me that the 'visitors' came two or three times a week in the dead of night, maybe so they can find me home – but why me? I ain't done nobody no harm, I'm just an honest citizen with an honest job trying to make an honest living. Yes I do have opinions, but so does everybody else and lemme tell you something, my opinion is like a drop in the ocean, it don't require late-night visitations for clarification and besides, I only air my views to friends and family and I don't even think anybody cares what I say. You see, where I come from in the southern part of Africa, late-night 'visitors' cannot be reasoned with nor can one negotiate with them, when you see them do the va-va-voom and don't look back …

I took a late lunch break one day and as I was enjoying my lemon'n'herb quarter chicken from Nando's and a milkshake from Creamy Inn, my phone rang and it was the boss himself. He told me not to come back to work that day and not even in the near future, he was going to send someone with my stuff to where I was right away. The anger that consumed me was unmentionable – after all I was the most hard-working and my department was flourishing, in fact a few weeks earlier I had gotten a raise. I couldn't finish my food. However when the messenger arrived and told me the full version, anger turned to fear. I was literally shaking – the 'visitors' had come to my workplace.

What? How? When? You know the one-word questions you ask in such situations. I knew I had to get outta there and fast so we withdrew all our savings and without telling a soul, not even mom and dad, we landed at Gatwick Airport.

I Guarantee

William G. Mbwembwe

I guarantee that you will be safe going to Zimbabwe
But I cannot guarantee your safety when you get there
I can guarantee that there is freedom of speech in Zimbabwe
But I cannot guarantee freedom after your speech
I can guarantee, all basic commodities are in plenty supply
You only have to read the paper and listen to the news
I can guarantee, the rate of crime is very low in Zimbabwe
Everybody is into it, it's the norm
I can guarantee, fuel is plenty-plus in Zimbabwe
Always at a filling station at the other side of town
I can guarantee free and fair elections in Zimbabwe
You are free and have a very fair chance
To vote for the ruling party
I can guarantee you a long life in Zimbabwe
Just don't carry this poem around with you.

(March 2005)

The Angelic Faces

William G. Mbwembwe

Melancholy, that's the word
There ain't no joy coz it's all so sad
The evil, the ugly and the very bad
So don't start with me coz this makes me mad

But if it is love, then why do we run away
And why would I be here today?
It is purely evil when you smile
When the children go hungry, and when they cry

"They colonised us ..." is an old Chimurenga song
Coz this is wrong, this is so wrong
Even being forced to sing "Pamberi ne" just to get the daily feed
You're like a goodly apple with a rotten inside

When there ain't no cash you say let's talk
Let there be a bumper harvest – you tell me to walk

I wanna know, so tell me pliz
How do you feel when you see all this?
And after you're through with all your analysis ...
How 'bout the children ... the angelic faces?

"Chimurenga": "the Struggle" against colonialism.
"Pamberi ne" ("Forward with ...") is a political slogan song.

Claiming Asylum is World-wide

Million Gashaw Woldemariam

First I will mention what I observed when I was claiming asylum in Croydon on March 25, 2002. Before I claimed asylum in the UK I had wrong ideas about who is a refugee or an asylum seeker. But after some time I was able to understand the definition of these terms.

In the course of claiming asylum I had to get to Croydon. When I arrived, there were long queues of people waiting their turn to enter Immigration. I became confused, because there were a lot of people in the queue, and approximately 80% of them were white people. I wondered if they were all working in the Home Office Immigration department.

I saw a police officer at the front of the queue, guiding and disciplining as appropriate, and I tried to get some information from him about how to make an asylum claim. He told me that all the people in the queue were there for the asylum claiming process, and he advised me to join the queue like the others. I did as I had been advised. Even though there were such a lot of people waiting to claim asylum, the process was so fast that I soon had the opportunity to enter Immigration.

As I began claiming asylum, I saw a fellow countryman who was working there. I told him where I was from, and mentioned how I had been surprised to see that a lot of white people were there claiming asylum. Because I thought that, most of the time, only black Africans are in danger of being subjected to persecution and harassment in their country of origin! However, he told me that people from different continents, of many different races, ethnic groups or nationalities, apply for asylum because of a well-founded fear of persecution due to their race, religion, nationality, political opinion or membership of a social group.

After applying for asylum, I was dispersed to Swansea by the National Asylum Support Service (NASS). In Swansea, where I am living with other asylum seekers, one morning I was explaining the situation I observed in Croydon to one of the other asylum seekers. At the time, we were both trying to prepare breakfast. I remember this guy was trying to fry an egg. I observed that he took an egg, broke it with a spoon, and then he put the egg-shell in the frying-pan and threw the yolk and white into the rubbish bin. I said to him: "What are you doing?" He answered:

"What I am doing?" Then I told him he was doing vice versa, the yolk in the bin, the shell in the frying-pan. Then he became aware of his mistake and said: "Oh my God, I am going to be crazy!" I tried to cool him down. Finally he told me that he had got a Refusal from the Home Office, and since then he was in constant fear.

It is terrible. Isn't it?

Sorry, I Was Miles Away

Million Gashaw Woldemariam

That green car's loud horn awakened me from day-dreaming in the street of Swansea. The driver was shouting and swaearing at me. Within a fraction of a second, I realized I was crossing the road unsafely.

On Tuesday, 5th of May, 2009, I was walking from the Uplands area on Walter Road in Swansea. As I walked along the road I noticed new buildings, Swansea changing, but my life stays the same. I racked my brain trying to search for the child of the past in me and figure out about my current miserable existence.

Even though I am not a religious person, sometimes I have an experience in which I feel spiritually gifted. In those euphoric moments, I feel like God or some higher power may be communicating with me. Somehow, since I arrived in Swansea, asylum seeking has been making my life a hell and I have been suffering great pain for solid seven years.

As I crossed Walter Road, I was thinking and pondering my past experiences and present bitter and hard-to-bear situation with no clue about the future. Thus, my conscious left brain shut down and I became totally immersed in my subconscious right brain. It was like ten seconds reverse hypnosis.

I think the gentleman behind the wheel was embarrassed by my strange situation. His final question to me was: "What the hell is the matter with you?" Then my answer was: "Sorry Sir, I was miles away!" He didn't say anything; just drove off fast.

<Million Gashaw Woldemariam was a highly qualified aeronautical engineer and flight safety inspector working in civil aviation in Ethiopia when he sought asylum in the UK in 2002, fleeing forced conscription into the military. He wrote "Claiming Asylum is World-wide" for *Between a Mountain and a Sea* (2003). He wrote the second text – "Sorry, I Was Miles Away" – in 2010 and used it as the basis for a short film which he made with the OnePeople community video project. The Home Office took eight and a half years to decide to grant him asylum. During that time Million's professional skills became useless and he suffered greatly from depression, and from the separation from his family in Ethiopia and daughter in the Ukraine. He is now a British citizen and is studying for an advanced certificate in software systems engineering and CISCO network engineering.

>Kate Bosse-Griffiths was born in Lutherstadt-Wittenberg (Germany) in 1910 and died in Swansea in 1998. She obtained a doctorate for research on Egyptian figures, but when the Nazis came to power she lost her post at a Berlin museum because her mother was of Jewish origin. Her mother was killed at Ravensbrück concentration camp. Other family members were interned but luckily survived. Kate was able to find refuge in England before the war, and then came to Wales to marry J. Gwyn Griffiths, who was also an Egyptologist. She learned Welsh, and published several books of short stories, novels, and travel books in Welsh, as well as a book on German pacifist movements, published in 1942. She became Keeper of Archaeology at Swansea Musuem and continued her Egyptological interests through her responsibility for the Wellcome Collection, which is now housed in the Egypt Centre at Swansea University.

Her son, Heini Gruffudd, is a celebrated Welsh language activist, publisher and educator. Heini made a major contribution as a translator and proof-reader to our bilingual collection *Gŵyl y Blaidd / Festival of the Wolf* (2006).

A Seed

Kate Bosse-Griffiths

(To answer the question, how could I have roots in two countries.)

I am a seed from a distant land
swallowed by a wandering bird
taken over the sea by a swallow
It descended on newly ploughed land
and threw out roots
I am a blade of grass on green pasture
bent under sheeps' hooves
chewed by a bullock's teeth
I grew into living flesh
I grew to be a part of Wales

3-1-1971, Swansea

Hedyn

Kate Bosse-Griffiths

(I ateb y cwestiwn, sut y gallwn berchen gwreiddiau mewn dwywlad.)

Hedyn wyf o wlad bell
wedi ei lyncu gan aderyn treigl
wedi ei gludo dros y môr gan wennol
Disgynnodd ar dir newydd ei aredig
a thaflu gwreiddiau
Glaswelltyn wyf ar borfa las
wedi fy mhlygu gan garn defaid
wedi fy nghnoi gan ddant bustach
Tyfais yn gnawd byw
Tyfais yn rhan o Gymru

3-1-1971, Abertawe

Gwenoliaid

Menna Elfyn

Fe ddeallwn wenoliaid,
briwsion ar fwrdd yr ardd,
yn llygad y drws.
Deallwn eu llwgu,
eu hawydd i dorri bara â ni.

Ac onid adar ydym ninnau,
adar nid o'r unlliw?
Eto'r entrych yw'r encil,
unigedd, cyn cyfannedd,
torcalon yn pigo'r pridd.

Ac ym mhob ffurfafen
mae mudo, cymysgu
â'r ddaear am nodded.
Fforddolion ar aden,
eu clwyfo gan hanes,
yn chwilio o'r newydd, nyth,
man gwyn i orffwys.

Yr adar, a'u plu cynnes?
Dylent gofio yr heb-ogion,
yn serio'r tir,
yn chwilio'r tir comin.

Un wên, a wna wanwyn,
un wennol yn llunio'r haf.

Swallows

Menna Elfyn

Birds we understand,
spend crumbs in garden,
at back-door's eye;
understand their need
to break bread with us.

And are we not birds who
don't always flock together?
The sky a high refuge,
lonely, knowing we'll land, meet
beak's needs, at heartbreak.

And in every firmament
migrators mingle, mixing
heaven and earth for shelter,
wayfarers a-wing,
histories' hurted,
seeking anew a nest,
a fair resting-place.

So those birds, warm-feathered,
should remember the withouters
scouring the soil
in search of common ground.

One smile a spring,
one swallow making summer.

< **Menna Elfyn** is the writer in Welsh best known outside Wales. Born in 1952, a much travelled and passionate campaigner on Welsh and international issues, she describes herself as a Christian anarchist. Besides plays, television dramas and a novel, she has published ten volumes of poetry, including the bilingual collections *Eucalyptus: Detholiad o Gerddi / Selected Poems 1978–1994* (Gomer), *Cell Angel* and *Cusan Dyn Dall / Blind Man's Kiss* (Bloodaxe). She both wrote and translated "Gwenoliaid" ("Swallows") specially for *Between a Mountain and a Sea*. Her website is: www.mennaelfyn.com

> **Hadi** came from Syria to the UK in 2012 and to Swansea in 2013. He has recently been granted five years leave to remain in the UK and hopes to continue his studies: he studied accountancy in Syria and intends to study economics in Swansea.

Small Fish From Syria

Hadi

Too many questions in my mind ... I can't sleep ... Why am I here!?

Everything started 2 years ago ... When we went out to the streets and
squares!

The people said: That's enough! Mafia get out!

The answer was killing and torture

4 friends said: Freedom! ... One of them is still alive

I felt fear ... I ran away to a safe land

He was waiting for me ... He took me to his friend's house

I thought a story had finished ... I didn't know it was starting

He made me a waiter for his guests ... I trusted him, he was from my
country!

I understood: Big fish eat small fish ... It makes no difference where you
are

It makes a difference who you are

Outside ... Wonder ... Life ... What I can do ...? Until a kind lady told
me

I went to the Refugee Council ... They moved me to Wales

Now I know what "asylum seekers" means

So if you read this story ... Now you know what I mean

(Swansea, March 2013)

Tears Also Have Something to Say

Zhila Irani

It has been scientifically proven that the ingredients in tears caused by chopping an onion or by gas or dust in the air, are different to tears that are emotionally induced. The emotions affect the hormones which in turn produce enzymes that stimulate the glands which then produce the tears.

I remember my mother asked me once: 'Do you know which is the most important part of the body?' I answered 'the ears', but she told me that without ears you are able to live a normal life – many successful people are deaf. After a while, my perception of the world changed and I thought the answer was the eyes, but she told me 'No. Some blind people have high levels of perception and lead fulfilling lives'.

When my father passed away, and I was crying on her shoulder, she said: 'Now you've found the most important part of your body. Your shoulders are very important because they can be somebody's refuge for tears and somebody else's shoulder can be yours, this is very important when you are very sad or in pain.'

She wished that I would never be alone and would always have shoulders to cry on. A normal friend never sees your tears but the shoulders of a real friend will be wet from your tears. I now realised that tears also have a place and something to say, something that we have to find and understand.

When my mother passed away, I found a shoulder to cry on, but still my tears have something to say! My pain has not been relieved but rather has accumulated. When people's freedom is denied and chains are on their mouths and pens, expressing yourself is a crime and even the basic requirements for life as a human being don't exist. The only wish is to break free from such a despotic situation, even if it's highly unlikely in the near future. In such a situation people will use their tears to draw a picture of their lives, their pains and their wishes. In the vacuum of passion and hope they will find tears a good companion, the best signal of speech.

The passion and symbolism of speech is like the flow of music. The music of tears is beyond the magic of imagination. We have to know that tears are innate, an international language which we did not need to learn. Everybody can understand this language. Tears have no geographical borders. Inside, however, tears are the borders between absolute darkness and a spark of hope for life and the future. All people in their tears are looking for what they have lost.

Open your eyes to believe that you are not alone.

<Zhila Irani is a pseudonym. Her article (first published in *Fragments from the Dark*, 2008) is based on one which she wrote for a women's magazine in Tehran. Its combination of science, emotion and politics did not please the Iranian authorities. Zhila came to Wales with her husband and children seeking asylum in 2002. She has meanwhile gained higher degrees in management and science.

>Michael Mokako came to Swansea in 2003 with his mother and sisters, seeking asylum from Congo-Kinshasa. He knew no English when he came, but soon wrote poems which we published in *Nobody's Perfect* and *Soft Touch*, and has meanwhile become a well-known rapper, DJ and club events manager.

From Nothing to Something

Michael Mokako

Here I am thinking about how I will achieve my dreams
Struggling day to day trying to arrange a good future
I know a day will come when things will go my way
I can just feel the shine, soon it's going to be my time

I can feel myself travelling from nothing to something
Sometimes people try to bring me down but I ain't scared
Because nobody is stopping me following my dreams
Even if they say I'll never make it, whatever they say

Isn't going to put me down, I know one day I'll make it
Not today, not tomorrow, but one day, I'll win all the respect
That's been taken and I'll become somebody

No matter what it's going to take
No matter what people are saying, I'll make it
Then I'll move from nothing to something

Bishopston Valley

Gabriel Lenge Vingu

Were I to forget all of the places and landscapes in Swansea, never would I forget Bishopston Valley;

were I to forget the Arches Hotel, which put me up in such abysmal fashion in Swansea for eight months, far from me the thought of forgetting you, Bishopston Valley;

were I to speak five times of the hardship, the difficulties and the suffering endured in Swansea as an asylum seeker, I would speak a thousand times of the solace and the joy experienced in Bishopston Valley;

valley who brought solace to my heart and filled it with joy in place of the sadness and anxiety created by the negative realities of the phenomenon of seeking asylum;

Bishopston Valley! You shall remain everlastingly engraved upon my memory!

The first time I visited you it was thanks to a walk led by Mr Ray Diddams, accompanied by his partner Olive Davies, their friends Sheila Manning and Sylvie Hoffmann, and her daughter Maria Williams, all of them people of good faith, and full of love for the asylum seekers living in Swansea, God's blessing be upon Ray, Olive, Sheila, Sylvie and Maria her daughter, for having given me the opportunity to visit you, Bishopston Valley;

when I think of the beautiful stream flowing through you, the hills and woods which make you, I shall pray to God to bless Swansea because of you, oh! Bishopston Valley, you filled me with intense joy, may my joy abide!

I remember when we arrived by the small stream that flows through the valley, and when I exclaimed: "Oh! What a wonderful stream, Sylvie!" – "Yes Gabriel, it is a beautiful nature reserve," replied Sylvie. – "Indeed, Sylvie. This stream is exactly like a stream that runs through Kizauvete Valley, a valley in Democratic Congo where I met up with my father and saw him for the last time, in Africa, in the year 2000." – "Are your father and mother still living today?" Sylvie asked. – "Yes, they are still alive today and I still remember my father, and praise him for showing manly courage, in that he did not let his tears flow much as we were saying goodbye to each other that last day of seeing one another, as my mother had shed a great quantity of tears, unable to restrain herself on that last day, when we were saying goodbye, as I was preparing to leave the land of my ancestors." Stunned, Sylvie was attentively following my words, and I continued: "I still remember well that last day when I saw my father, by the stream that flows through Kizauvete Valley, so exactly like this stream that flows through Bishopston Valley; on that day, my father and I had washed our clothes in the stream and laid them out on the stones to dry, and we were sitting near the stream, speaking of everything and nothing, when my father asked me this: 'Are you thirsty, Gaby?' I answered: 'Yes, papa, extremely thirsty,' thinking that my father had a bottle of mineral water in his bag. He replied: 'Well, go down to the stream and drink the water from the stream!' – 'Drink water from the stream? No, papa, I cannot drink that water!' – 'Why not?' said my father, 'This water comes from a spring, it's pure, clean water.' – 'It's very dirty and murky, papa. It's not purified.' – 'You are wrong, my son. This water comes from a spring, it is well filtered, well purified, naturally, as it passes through the rocks.' – 'No, papa, I'm scared of catching a disease.' – 'No, no, this water will do you no harm. Watch me, now I'm drinking it,' and my father drank the spring water in the stream and did not die, and then he said: 'Here, take, drink. I've been drinking this water for 55 years, each and every time I come to the village I drink this water and it does me no harm. Drink!' he said; and so, to please my father, I drank the water, and my father said: 'So, Gaby, are you dead?' 'No,' I replied. 'Good. This experience will help you wherever you go,' concluded my father."

"It's a beautiful story, Gabriel, thank you for sharing it with me," Sylvie commented. "Yes, Sylvie. A living human being always has a story to tell, for someone with no story to tell cannot be said to be a human being." With her silence, Sylvie left me time to speak and I continued: "Today I am recording another story from my life, the story of the walk in Bishopston Valley, a valley which has been visited in the past, and today was visited by me, and will be visited by others in the future. May the blessing of God be upon you, oh! Bishopston Valley, you who were the place of my joy and my solace in Swansea, and I shall never forget you, oh! Bishopston Valley!"

< Gabriel Lengu Vingu came from Angola to the UK seeking sanctuary in 2001. His case was not accepted and he was deported five years later, having survived on no public support at all during most of his time in the UK. He is a pastor of the Pentecostalist Church. He walked in Bishopston Valley, as described in his story, on 16 March 2003. He wrote the story on 20 April, at the instigation of Sylvie Hoffmann, who translated it from French. It appeared in *Between a Mountain and a Sea*.

Gabriel responded to a Welsh landscape in a way which resonates with poetry a thousand years old.

> Anonymous ancient Welsh-language poets wrote "Canu Heledd" ("Songs of Heledd") and "Claf Abercuawg" ("Afflicted, Abercuawg") approximately 11 or 12 hundred years ago. The authors are not known.

Heledd is thought to be a Welsh tribal princess from present-day Shropshire, most of whose family were slaughtered by invading English tribes.

The speaker of "Claf Abercuawg" is an outcast, an exile, literally or metaphorically a leper. Tom adapted the translations by Jenny Rowland in *Early Welsh Saga Poetry: A Study and Edition of the Englynion*, 1990.

These poems are a reminder that experiences of becoming and being a refugee are universal and far from new.

from Heledd's Songs – Canu Heledd

I am called wandering Heledd.
Oh God, who has taken
My brothers' horses and their land?

...

Thin the breeze, thick the misery.
The furrows remain; their makers do not.
So piteous that those who were are no more.

...

In the time when they were fair
The daughters of Cyndrwyn were loved:
Heledd, Gwladus and Gwenddwyn.

I had lovely sisters.
I lost them, every one of them:
Ffreuer, Meddwyl and Meddlan.

I also had sisters.
I lost them all together:
Gwledyr, Meisir and Ceinfryd.

...

Afflicted, Abercuawg – Claf Abercuawg

My spirit craves to sit a long time on a hill,
Not that I will up and go:
My journey now is short, my home desolate.

Piercing the wind in this barren place.
The woods dress in summer's fair colours.
I lie feverish today.

Doing nothing, unaccompanied,
Unable to get out.
The cuckoo is pleased to sing.

In Abercuawg the cuckoos sing
On flowering branches.
Woe to the listener lying sick.

In Abercuawg the cuckoos sing.
To my heart it is wretched
That one who heard them now hears nothing.

I hear the cuckoo on an ivy-covered tree
And tug at my clothes
In grief for all I loved.

High above the great oak
I heard birds singing there.
Noisy cuckoo, all remember lost loves.

Endless song, full of longings,
Leave-takings, plunging like a hawk:
The loud cuckoo of Abercuawg.

Noisy the birds, damp the valleys.
Moon shines at chill midnight.
Sore sickness makes my heart raw.

Noisy the birds, damp the valleys,

Long the night. What's rare is praised,
And I deserve the reward of age: sleep.

Noisy the birds, wet the shingle.
Leaves fall, the exile's spirits falter.
Tonight I'm sick indeed.

Noisy the birds, wet the shore,
Bright the sky, generous the wave.
Longing withers the heart.

Noisy the birds, wet the shore,
Bright the generous motion of the wave.
What the boy loved, the man longs for again.

Noisy the birds on the highlands of Edrywy.
Loud the cry of the hounds hunting the moor.
Noisy the birds again.

Hilltop hazy; tip of ash-tree slender.
Shining waves roll out of estuaries.
Laughter is far from my heart.

Today is the end of my month
In this abandoned hostel.
My heart is raw. Fever has me.

Cattle in the shed, mead in the bowl.
Wisdom avoids strife, patiently
Forging a bond of understanding.

Cattle in the shed, ale in the bowl.
Slippery the paths, fierce the down-pour.
Danger at the ford. Treachery in mind.

Treachery's a mind-made evil.
Grief comes with atonement, swapping
For a little thing, a great one.

So much wickedness.
On Judgment Day
Only the true will shine bright.

Cups are lifted, an enemy defeated,
Men make merry over ale.
The stalks are withered. The cattle in the shed.

I have heard the heavy wave pound
Loud between the shingle and the beach.
My heart is raw with misery tonight.

The oak-tree tip branches. Bitter tastes the ash.
Sweet the cow-parsley root. Laughing the wave.
My face reveals my heart's distress.

The leper was a squire, a bold warrior
At a king's court.
May God be kind to the outcast.

Rough Guide

Grahame Davies

It happens inevitably,
Like water finding its level:
Every time I open a travel book,
I sail past the capital cities, the sights,
And dive straight in to the backstreets of the index
To find that in France, I'm Breton,
In New Zealand, Maori;
In the USA – depending on which part –
I'm Navajo, Cajun, or black.

I'm the Wandering Welshman.
I'm Jewish everywhere.
Except, of course, in Israel.
There, I'm Palestinian.

It's some kind of complex, I know,
That makes me pick this scab on my psyche.
I wonder sometimes what it would be like
To go to these places
And just enjoy.

No, as I wander the continents of the guidebooks,
Whatever chapter may be my destination,
The question's always the same when I arrive:
"Nice city. Now where's the ghetto?"

< **Grahame Davies** was brought up in Wrexham. He is a poet, editor and literary critic, working both in Welsh and in English. He is the author of 16 books including *The Chosen People* (2002), a study of the relationship between the Welsh and Jewish peoples, and *The Dragon and the Crescent* (2011), a study of connections between Wales and Islam. Grahame co-edited the bilingual collection *Gŵyl y Blaidd / Festival of the Wolf* (Hafan Books and Parthian, 2006): that was a huge task which included translating all the English-language poems, stories and extracts in the book into Welsh, and most of the Welsh-language texts into English. His poem "Rough Guide" is from the bilingual collection *Ffiniau / Borders*, by Elin ap Hywel and Grahame Davies (2002).

> **Howard David Ingham** came to Swansea from England as a student in 1994 and has stayed here, working as a writer, editor and performer. He was artist in residence at Swansea University in 2012-13.

A Round of Applause for the Volunteer from the Audience

Howard David Ingham

(after Sophie Nield)

The illusionist is smiling, but he never looks the part:
No hat, no hoops, no handkerchiefs, no rabbits,
No deck of cards in which to shuffle me;
His only act this one steel box,
I the volunteer, this disappearing trick:
First my savings, and then my name,
No magic wand, two rods clang into place
　　　　And I am gone.
No fanfare; a partial reappearance
On some foreign asphalt path,
Papers in my hand I cannot read:
　　　　Is this your card?
Now you see me.

In memoriam Kalan Kawa Karim

Jeni WIlliams

A fine day for the march. The curious
watched from doorways then walked off to unknown
busy lives, bored with chant and furious
protest. But, by the roadside and alone

for the quiet minute's length, an old man
slowly uncovered his head. He looked down,
acknowledging the brief and shattered span
of a good life, then left. No speech in town

denouncing such purposeless violence,
moved me so much as that man standing there,
head bent, holding his cap, the small silence
growing all round us. We walked to the square

and the cars, which had paused for the event,
moved on into a new, sunlit moment.

Kalan Kawa Karim was Kurdish and came from Dohuq, in Iraq. He took part in Kurdish resistance against the rule of Saddam Hussein and was shot and wounded, jailed and tortured by Iraqi forces. He was granted asylum in the UK and moved to Swansea in 2003 to be with his brother, who was claiming asylum. Karim was hoping to be reunited with his wife. He followed the Swansea World Stars football team, associated with SBASSG. He was 29 years old when he was killed in a racially motivated assault in the early hours of 6 September 2004 in Swansea city centre. His killer, a Swansea man of no fixed address, was convicted of manslaughter and served a prison sentence of 5 years. Karim's death galvanised support for refugees in Swansea. Over a thousand people joined a silent march through the town centre. *Soft Touch* (Hafan Books, 2005) was dedicated to Karim's memory, and included three poems written in response to his death.

< **Jeni Williams** is a poet, writer, teacher, lecturer, and a longstanding volunteer for Asylum Justice, the charity based in Swansea which has provided much-needed free legal services for thousands of people seeking sanctuary since 2003. Jeni co-edited *Fragments from the Dark* (Hafan Books, 2008) with Latéfa Guémar, and has helped inspire and/or translate many of the poems in this book too.

> **Richard 'Rej' Jones** was a teacher, a poet, a socialist and a chess player, among many other things. He came to Swansea from St Albans (England) in the 1960s to study politics, then worked for thirty years as a schoolteacher in secondary schools in the Swansea area. He was always active in the trades union movement and anti-racist and anti-war movements. In his poetry blog and book, both called "A Fistful of Poetry", he fought for national and international causes, against oppression and bigotry, with the weapons of anger, wisdom and humour. Blog and book survive as his epitaphs.

Give Me Your Hand Kalan Kawa Karim

Richard Jones

Give me your hand Kalan Kawa Karim:
Unfamiliar with my wasted land,
Not seeing the pools of sickness around you,
You dream of mountainous horizons

To be climbed slowly, ignoring the pains
That nag every step on the way back home.
They call this road The Kingsway. You ask why
There are no monuments to their greatness,

Being used to statues in any open square,
His face everywhere you dare to raise your eyes,
The penetrating stare that reached where
None could hear your desperate futile cries.

You smile. The last time you saw him he looked
Like that tea-cosy tramp in the garden.
His slack jaw gaped helpless for all to see.
Even a tramp showed greater dignity

Than this fallen torturer. Your heart leapt
Knowing the return journey could begin.
Take the first steps then, past The Potter's Wheel,
Feel your face fresh in the breath of sea wind.

Give me your hand Kalan Kawa Karim:
There is yet one more dark night to cross
And though all time here they sing of welcomes,
Still fear strikes down the man who dares to dream.

St Phillip's Saturday – Matchday

Sean Barr

Kick off is at 3 o'clock (ish)
The venue? Up the stairs…
Kids ready for their footie fix
Rearranging chairs

To serve as goalposts or as sidelines
To even sit on too
Breathlessly rushing, kicking, pushing
Shouting "that's pen' proof"

Jabulani or maybe Tango or
Bouncing yellow foam
Knocked about by little kids
Dreaming far from home

Of vast arenas
Of post goal preening
Of adoring screaming
Of …… biscuit eating

I've heard the voices to Zadok chanting…
"They are the best"
"They have no equal"
No matter what they meant
3 o'clock in St Phillips
"That is the main event"

"Pen' proof" is playground slang: "penalty proof" in case of a disputed goal

< **Sean Barr** from Belfast works in Swansea University library and was the coach for Swansea World Stars (the football team of Swansea Bay Asylum Seekers Support Group) for several years. He currently coaches a Mumbles Rangers junior team and volunteers on Saturdays at SBASSG's drop-in at St Phillip's Community Centre. He wrote this poem in March 2013 "after some idiot chucked a brick through the window while the lads were playing football".

> **Becky Lowe** is a poet, peace activist and freelance journalist. She writes mostly about topical ethical issues, and has contributed features to the *South Wales Evening Post*, *Western Mail*, *Big Issue*, and many others. In 2008 her feature on human trafficking was shortlisted for a One World Media Award. She writes: "My poem 'Asylum' was inspired by reading about the experiences of asylum-seekers who are often forced into living in temporary accommodation. It is a poem about identity, cultural differences, and the pressure to conform to other people's perceived expectations."

Asylum

Becky Lowe

We live our lives
Out of suitcases; nowadays
We're getting smaller,
It used to take
A building to contain us,
Now we've shrunk
To these four
Battered corners.

I unpack myself,
So far, so very far
From where I've come from –
These little trinkets
Seem to vanish
Into the space
We're given,
There is less
And less of me
Each day.

So little to show
For the years I've spent –
Notebooks, pencils, photographs,
I wonder sometimes
If it might be easier
To throw it all away
And start again.

I could be anyone
You wanted, then,
Mould myself
To your contours
Until we fitted;
Instead, I'm constantly
Folding and unfolding
My wings like butterflies.

Love

Hanan Beko

If all the relationships in the world end
If all the stars in the sky are hidden

Your love in my heart is
A candle that will never go out

<Hanan Beko is from the Syrian part of Kurdistan. Mona Balbaki and Jeni Williams helped translate his poem – he has many more.

>Mona Balbaki was born in Sierra Leone in a Lebanese family and moved to the Lebanon when she was 14. She studied Nursery Education and worked as a nursery teacher. She married an Iraqi and came to the UK with him, seeking sanctuary. She is a qualified playworker and a key volunteer with Swansea Bay Asylum Seekers Support Group, running the drop-in kitchen most Fridays and organizing lots of trips and outings.

Dancing

Mona Balbaki

We dance
in the dark

Dancing in the moonlight
and walking out under the fresh trees
in fresh air

There are different kinds of flowers
tiny flowers, white, yellow, red...
The shadow of the leaves dark in the dark...
It's spring time...
The smell of jasmine, nerjes

Dancing in the motion of the music
feel the sound and warmth of it...
When you are alone
you feel the warmth of music

The sound of nature:
the creatures
the sound of birds, the bulbul

And the colour of the dark sky
which takes you to the end
and makes you move
step by step

The taste of mint in this lovely dark night
the taste of sweet in this slow-motion music...
See all these wonderful things
feel it never ends

The Seashore

Mona Balbaki

I remember one time
I walked by the seashore
early in the morning

I heard the birds sing…
The small green hassan
bright with purple and orange
called from the ekdenya trees

I heard the soft waves
one by one slowly breaking
slowly breaking on the smooth sand

I sat and played with the sand
writing memories
listening to the birds
round the houses and rocks

The salty taste of the sea

The cold breeze made me shiver a little
then I drank warm coffee, watching the sea

Thinking, my mind goes far away
floating, with my memories, over the sand

Part 2

Swansea Collages

Spoken words composed by Sylvie Hoffmann

Sylvie's "Swansea Collages" appeared in *Between a Mountain and a Sea*, *Nobody's Perfect*, and *Soft Touch*. These are 'found poems', based on conversations with people seeking sanctuary. Many (like Sylvie herself) are French-speakers: women, men and children from countries including Angola, Burundi, Cameroon, the Congo, Guinea, Mali, Rwanda and Sierra Leone.

Sylvie says: "They all prefer to remain anonymous. I have translated their poems as faithfully as I can."

Some of the pieces are based on Sylvie's experiences as an interpreter, occasionally paid, more often voluntary. For example, "Are You Happy With That" (at the front of this book).

Sylvie grew up in Lorraine, in France, and came to the UK in the 1970s, settling in the Swansea area. She became a teacher, an artist, a pilot, a poet, an interpreter, a mother and grandmother. She co-founded Hafan Books: this project could not have begun or continued without her. A collection of her poems and stories in English (and Welsh English) and French – *Across the Sound* – appeared in 2011.

A Gift for My Day

February 2013. Cold winter day. A black African man, about 50, dressed in rags, bare feet, was standing in the Quadrant bus station.

I went up to him: 'You're very brave to go out like that.'

He replied with a smile: 'You're the first person to speak to me since I arrived. That is why your heart is still beating.'

Behind the Facades

What is behind?
Is this a church?
No, no… it's a school
Is this a church?
No, no… it's an Indian restaurant
Is this a church?
No, no… it's the old Swansea police station

What is behind?
Is this a church?
Yes, this is a church
You can come in if you wish

The Community Comprehensive School

Four girls
Why treat my child so?
Why treat my child so?

"I'm a good listener" says the School...
It is true
We speak for three hours
Communication restored

Just Arrived

The cars
I am frightened
The streets
I am frightened
The sea
I am frightened
I am frightened for my children

Swansea Bandits

broken
glass
fires lit on the
hills
twelve-year-olds who
smoke
they like to
drink
telephone
bills
we have to pay yet do not call

The Docks

The ferry from Swansea to Cork
I wish…

I bitterly want to see Paris

At Home

We get up with the sun
We go to bed with the sun
No one sends us an electricity bill at the end of the month

The British

They say "sorry" but do they mean it?

In the Fish and Chips Shop

Broad smile:
– "Are you on holidays?"

Swansea Central Library

We send each other e-mails round the computer table
A good meeting place
A safe haven

Clyne Gardens

Do you have to pay to come in here?
No, no, it's free of charge

Here you can walk in peace and safety, play football, meditate… it's one
of Swansea's best kept secrets
In May the gardens are in full bloom, they are magnificent

It makes me nervous, this dog off its lead
Dogs should be on lead, some owners do not care

At the Kingsway Centre

How is your English coming along?
– "I must"

White Man

Never has any time
Rushes everywhere

"Incidents of racism are falling" (2)

Outside CK's supermarket,
High Street, February 2005:
Thumped, kicked, floored,
Knocked out for six – black bitch!

Swansea Wedding: the Fool's Tale

I saw the sun adorned with black ribbons
I saw red white and yellow flowers warming the street with light
I saw the cake tied to the shop window
I saw banners and balloons cut in western fashion
I saw cars arriving, deliciously cooked
I saw meat, fish and fruits, guests in dashing outfits
I saw men and women with the patience of angels
I saw children dancing the day away
I saw a blue dress walk with magnificence
I saw the bride and groom who saw these wondrous sights

Sketty

Scissors, paper and stone
Ministers at their pulpits
Politicians at their politics
Economists at their economics

We are here for something else!
We are here for something else!

Greetings

Mon ami	My friend
Mon pote	My mate
Mon coeur	My heart

The Tides

Ebb – *Llanw yn uchel*
"The old man 'it me on the 'ead"
Pardon?
"The old man 'it me on the 'ead"
Pardon?
"The OLD MAN 'IT ME ON THE 'EAD"

A llifo – And flow
Two young men from Cameroon…
Swansea Enforcement Unit
They came to get them in the middle of the night…
The way they knock! I was scared…
Do you need to knock like that?
What's that got to do with you, Boy?
I'm frightened…
Boy I'm frightened.

Low tide – *Llanw yn isel*

The M.P.'s surgery: interpretation

– What does she want me to write?
– Tell him I found no solicitor to take up my case.
Tell him where do I need to look?
Tell him I cannot pay for one myself.
Tell him I'm scared, my baby is babbling but I am scared.
– What does she want me to write?

Sunday Morning Patrol

On the way to church
Meet and greet in Humphrey Street
Police
He takes his time
Car parking   : checked
Car tyres   : checked
Sellotape holding petrol cap : checked
Driver's licence   : checked
Driver's address   : checked
Driver's date of birth   : checked
Driver saved by her birthday
Granted leave to leave

Madhouse

That morning I left for college
I didn't know I'd not be coming back.
I took no belongings, no books, no clothes –
I did not know.
I'm lost here, utterly lost and bewildered.

Still in Swansea?

Yes, I'm still in Swansea.
Even when you're destitute
You don't shit in the saucepan that
You use to cook your food.

Roofless

– Where are you staying now?
– Oh, I haven't decided yet!
Prime ministers and presidents speak over my head.
Me, I want to stay in bed,
To sleep, sleep, since they won't let me work.
Sleep!
I want to sleep and die and yet I have to live.

Insomnia

Denounced – persecuted – exiled – dispersed –
Refused – sectioned – certified –
Now, how shall we proceed?

Insomnia

unable to switch off
lights on
eyes wide

The father: Till dawn I pace between four walls. I play with my children's keyboard. I try the bed, I try the settee, I try the floor … but I don't try the door. Outside, Swansea is dangerous …

The student: I cry, my lips tremble, I walk down the beach. Sure, I fear for my life, so I write, I write, I write …

The mother: I cannot go to sleep, I must stay awake, I need to protect my children …

The G.P.

This G.P., he won't examine me.
He examines my clothes instead,
He refuses to touch me.
He won't use Language Line.
He refuses to believe me.
He says I'm telling lies, he says I'm fine.
He gives me Prozac, a stronger dose each time.
It's destroying me, I cannot sleep.
They are the mad ones, not me.

Section 55: The parents' story

Our eldest daughter taken away from us!
Kept behind in London, no money, no food, nowhere
To live, on her own,
To be caught and sent back to be
Torn and abused by the military.
And yet they know!
Themselves, the British, they're
Shitting themselves to get out of the embassy.
We want her with us
We want her safe
We want her well
We want to care for her
We are not given the freedom
To love our own daughter.

Part 3

Writers in Motion

This section gathers together poems and other texts by writers who have come to Wales as asylum seekers or refugees – with a special emphasis on the word 'writers' here.

Some are (or were) professional writers, making a living from writing. For others, writing is an important passion, a talent they work hard to develop. In several cases, their writing caused or helped to cause the problems that let to them fleeing their country and seeking sanctuary abroad. They all have a body of impressive work. Here are just some samples.

In addition to problems of finding good translators, or finding publishing opportunities for work which is mostly not very 'commercial', many writers who are refugees, or exiles, or seekers of sanctuary, are wary of publishing at all.

For example, one writer of great talent, who comes from a country in the Middle East and lives in South Wales, is not represented here. She has asked us not to publish any of her short stories in this book, because they are highly critical of the regime in her country, and she fears that there could be dangerous repercussions for members of her family living in, or planning to visit, that country.

So it is that the censorship that is applied in many countries works far beyond their borders.

> **Mahmood Ahmadifard** has a Masters in Business and Accountancy from Tehran University. His poetry was part of the reason why he fled the Islamic Republic of Iran: he had a book published, then it was banned and pulped. He came to the UK with his wife and two young children in 2004. They waited several years for a Home Office decision but eventually were granted refugee status and are now UK citizens. Mahmood has qualified as an electrician and plumber and set up a solar panel installation company, while his wife has resumed her career as a research scientist. His poems were translated by Parvin Leloi.

Foreigner

Mahmood Ahmadifard

This is Iran, the land of the Persians,
The land of Cyrus the Great,
The land of Darius and Xerxes.

An ancient people, a great people,
A familiar land, my country.

It is the land of the Sun, of the God of Love,
And thousands of years later
It is a land of cruelty and revolt.

The land of Gods is a despotic empire
Where workers are unpaid and bosses pillage – thieves!

Here even the trees are afflicted,
And the breeze, the spring, the harvest too, the rain.
Here the red roses of affection have perished, and
The Sun of Love is bereft of its warmth.

The nightingales no longer sing of freedom.
The little flower-messengers bring no more happy news.
Here the measure of ability and skill consists in
Absolute obedience and silence.
Here even whispering is forbidden!

This is Iran,
A foreign land, an unfamiliar land, strange, alien!

Unexplained

Mahmood Ahmadifard

In this painless time
Of what pain should I complain?
Of what sorrow should I sing?
When pain and grief are stories not to be told,
When only grief rises from the innermost soul!

Bite the Dust

Mahmood Ahmadifard

message from cold silent history
along the path of time
                              from a hard time
like a spaceship
                penned in by night
                              a beam of light
                              among the stars
make your way
        let light be our desire
find a captain
                        escape the darkness
morning comes
those who choose freedom
                over evil
those who choose to bite the dust
                over living a lickspittle life
a time machine
                              among ruins
                no bread
                pain in
orphan eyes
seekers of utopia
        show yourselves
                find a leader
                        gather for strength
                        clasp hands
wherever whenever tyrants
                steal freedom
                        let them know we are there

> **Amani Omer Bakhiet Elawad** was born in Sudan and now lives in Swansea. She is a mother of four. In Sudan, she studied Agricultural Economics, took a Postgraduate Diploma in Development Planning, then took a Masters in Agricultural Economics. She worked in a number of high-level management and research posts, including as researcher and deputy manager with the Alfanar Organization for Development and Capacity Building, before she and her family had to flee. Her poem "I Journey Toward You" was made into a moving video produced by OnePeople. The poems were translated by Amani with Jeni Williams.

و تقول

لن اكتُبَكِ بعد الآن قصيده
و هل يعبّركَ الشوقُ دونَ سطور
تعزفُ نبضاً... تسطعُ بوحاً
راية صدق... تصدحّ حينا
لحناً صاغ الوجد معاني فريده

و هل تُنبنكَ حروفي انكَ روحي
قلبي و ذاتي.. تهبّ ثباتي
سُحباً تُمطرُ عشقاً دافئ
فيض فاق حدودَ الوصف.. و الكلماتِ
حُلماً اهدي العمر ليالي سعيده

و يكفي أنك بين ضلوعي
مدّ يعبّر عُمقَ حدودي
رمزٌ حددَ شكلَ وجودي
فجرٌ حطمَ طوقَ يودي
ليبقى حبَك فوقَ الكلمهِ اقوى مني
و تَبقى لكل صباح طلة عِيده

And You Say

Amani Omer Bakhiet Elawad

And you say
you will write no more poems.

How can my tenderness utter itself without verses
that set your heartbeats to a music shimmering with ardour?
Truth reveals itself in melodies
whose harmonies frame passion in pure intensity.

Do my letters prove that you are my soul, my heart, my being?
that in your presence I discover myself?

The clouds rain warm love,
the flood spills over my words and writings:
your love gifts my life with the happiness of dream.

It is enough that you lie at the core of my soul:
a tide breaching my deepest boundaries,
a star drawing my shape to fuller existence.

Your love is greater than these words, stronger than me:
you are the dawn of my every Eid morning.

اليك ارتحل
قوافلا تسارع الخطي
تسابق الزمن

اليك ارتحل
عوالماً لأجلك
تعانق الهوي تفارق الشجن

اليك ارتحل
روائعاً بحبك
توقع الغناء
تصطفي رحاب صدرك

اليك ارتحل
جوانحاً لقربك
تداعب الصباح
تحتمي بنور صدرك

اليك ارتحل
سواحلاً مشوقه
تغازل السحاب
تشتهي مياه بحرك

اليك ارتحل
اليك ارتحل

I Journey Towards You

Amani Omer Bakhiet Elawad

I journey towards you
joining the fastest caravan,
seeking to overtake time.

I journey towards you.
I will give you new worlds
with the recovery of love, the loss of suffering.

I journey towards you.
Miracles will be inspired by your love,
marvellous songs will choose
the wide space of your breast to be their home.

I journey towards you
to be close to you,
to be cradled by wings in the morning of love,
to shelter in the light of your dawn.

I journey towards you.
The passionate beaches
ache to touch the clouds.
They crave the waters of your ocean.

I journey towards you.
I journey towards you.

>**Abdallah Bashir-Khairi** was born on Dagarty Island in the Nile, near Karma, Sudan. He studied medicine at Juba University and practised psychiatry in the Sudan and Qatar before coming to the UK seeking sanctuary in 1998. Granted leave to remain, he took an MSc at Cardiff University and worked in the Wales Asylum Seeking and Refugee Doctors Programme (which identified 115 qualified medical doctors among asylum seekers in Wales in 2002-5) and a research project on mental health and social needs among ethnic minorities in Cardiff. Dr Bashir-Khairi left the UK for Qatar in summer 2004.

His stories have been published in Arabic in magazines in London and Qatar, where his first collection – *Al-Ruyia* (The Vision) – appeared in 2004. The stories published here were translated from the Arabic by Ibrahim Gafar, a philosopher and writer living in London, and edited by Tom Cheesman. They recount episodes in the civil war in Sudan from 1983 to 2005.

"This, or the Deluge...!" describes the 'White Procession' in Khartoum in 1985, a peaceful protest by the democratic movement known as the Republican Brothers. The movement opposed the Sudanese regime and its imposition of sharia law. It was led by Ustaz Mahmoud Mohamed Taha (1909-85), 'Africa's Ghandi'. Arrested for distributing a pamphlet titled "This, or the Deluge", Taha was tried and executed for heresy. See www.alfikra.org

"The Text Committee" is satire based in truth. A "Tribunal Committee for Textual Rectification" is responsible for state censorship in Sudan. Since the military coups of 1985 and 1989 and the imposition of sharia law, it has been an instrument of oppression. Sibawayh "the Phonologist" was a great early scholar of the Arabic language (8th century AD). The popular drama "The Cock of Al-Hajja Bahana", by Adel Ibrahim, really did fall foul of the censors. "The Wanderer" is an unpublished novel by a friend of the author. Other literary examples are invented. The "Literary Society" of the story is based on the Sudanese Society for the Humanities, which published the magazine *Horouf* (*Letters*) in 1988-9 until the regime closed them down. One of the author's articles, due to have been published in the magazine, was confiscated and used against him in his interrogation.

This, or the Deluge...!

Abdalla Bashir-Khairi

Suddenly that evening, as I was beginning to turn my steps towards the far corner of the vast square at the centre of the city, I felt a constriction in my chest and an unusual commotion. Before I could complete my quick turn to face the other side of the square, I found myself in their hands.

The sun was bidding farewell to the quarters of the square; dusk was dragging the sun's golden tails in a slow and leisurely retreat towards its hidden sleeping-place, behind the distant horizon, beyond the Nile. I could no longer see the radiant faces and white robes of those who had committed themselves to beautifying the city streets with the roses and flowers of the New Thinking. I bade the city and them farewell in my thoughts and feelings. Since then I have seen neither it nor them. It was as if celestial carriages drawn by winged horses had transported them all, that evening, to invisible heavens – or so I consoled myself.

They severed the thread of my contemplation and bundled me into a Landrover, then deliberately confused my senses by taking a long, roundabout and zigzag route. At one moment we seemed to be passing over a river. I felt a whiff of a soothing draught of air waft over me, refreshing hope within me, despite the tight blindfold. The car stopped several times. Various exchanges took place between those inside it and others, all in the form of codes and riddles.

Finally we stopped at what seemed to be the destination. I was dragged along a long, damp hallway, half-walking, almost suffocating, roughly shoved, stumbling, until at last I arrived in a kind of circular room at the end of the hallway. There I was stripped of all of my clothes, cruelly beaten, flesh and bone, and I suffered – momentarily – humiliation. This was followed by hours of interrogation inside that damp room smelling of betrayal.

The face interrogating me was so sadistic that it seemed visibly to thrive on the sight of me twisting and convulsing under the whips of pain. It was as if that character had sprouted like a fungus from spores of professional crime and vileness. Or it seemed as though he was extracting from my flesh and my soul the price of an old vendetta, or exacting revenge for blood that had been shed unknown to me. It was a face absolutely isolated from any current of mercy and all that belongs with it: a maliciously ugly face, oozing with insult and the will to injure everything innocent.

They want to wrest a confession out of me? A confession of what? Of a conspiracy which they suspect? He handed me an exercise book and a pen, and with a glare which gathered all the menace of the world, in a coarse voice, home to all of cruelty's parasites, he said: "I want this back tomorrow morning, full of the names of all who were with you and with all the details of the conspiracy! No need for you to deny your knowledge of anything, our sources have left us in no doubt." He gave me a meaningful look as he shut the door behind himself: "Do what we ask of you, and we'll make you a prosecuting witness."

Rage possessed me and I shouted at him: "Some of us have met their Maker under your filthy hands, but those who still have that to come still do as they please under the sun and under the moon. Didn't you arrest us from a square at the heart of the city?"

My voice was lost to the wind and air: already he had locked the door behind him, slipping out without hearing me. I picked up the exercise book which he had left. But the pen had fallen and rolled away. I crawled towards it, exhausted to the extreme. My fingers groped their way towards it over the damp floor. When I was satisfied that my hand held the pen, as far as my worn-out strength permitted I straightened up, hugged the exercise book and pen to me and breathed the sweet repose of the enchanted passion of two intimate companions in an oasis in a desert of nothingness. I put the exercise book down on the ground and bent over it to write. My eyes were now used to the semi-darkness hovering over that place. Of which enough.

As I was immersed in writing, the door was half-opened. I didn't raise my face, but I heard him say: "We were sure you'd act like a rational, intelligent man." He closed the door behind him and disappeared, adding: "Keep on writing, and don't forget you'll be a key witness."

The sound of the door closing synchronised with a strange relaxation in my exhausted memory. I remembered how, when I was being beaten and kicked, I had rolled myself up and completely surrendered to the experience moment by moment. Exactly in that position I relived, in an enlightened and vivid way, the events of our historic procession, the White Procession which reclaimed the long road from Al-Mahdiyya to Sharfi Graveyard. I had been lucidly alive with the White Procession as it turned, following the road to the left to head past the Northern Police Station, and on towards Martyrs' Square at the heart of the city. The men were wearing white jallabiyyas and bright turbans, and the women were wearing white dresses. The procession was radiant, peaceful and wonderful. I particularly recollected how all of us, men and women, white-haired elderly and children, sat on the ground, when obstructed by the police, in a composed, reverent and sober manner, each person in his own place.

I rolled myself up more in an attempt to protect my sensitive organs from the humiliating, damaging kicking. The remembrance continued, alive and vivid. People gathered around us and on the rooftops of the houses, women and men astonished at our bright whiteness seeping down towards the square. So we poured on, a silent flow, from the left of Mahatma Gandhi Junction, into Nile Street, and under the eves of the Sudan Broadcasting Corporation building, where we were grievously shocked to see *them* giving a very old man an excruciating beating.

From there the procession headed through Khalifa's Square, to the court where the judges sat in a row, empty-hearted, holding their noses high, haughtily strangling themselves with their neck-ties, like some satanic beings which have emerged from a dark cosmic hole.

I cannot now remember anything further than that, and I no longer have the strength to continue this narration, for the mere act of evoking memories wears me out, and the remains of the candle's glimpses inside myself drip and fuse into a formless whole before, finally, being extinguished!

It doesn't matter. I am, inevitably, dying now. In just a few moments I will be irrevocably deceased, and my soul will have what is arguably the good fortune to observe the last stages of the hidden crime in my poor visible body lying on the ground, motionless.

Of course, my oppressor will be back for the exercise book, expecting to break the pen after forcing me to sign my name. But when he sees me a lifeless corpse, he'll be struck dumb, and his disappointment will rise as he understands that the exercise book is only an empty pad of pages eying him sarcastically. . .

The Court

Abdallah Bashir-Khairi

There was no space, not even a marginal one, to make room for the sad feelings which burgeoned inside me at that time. Nor could I find an answer for any of the tragic questions which were burning inside my mind. All that I could find was a solemn accusation directed by myself against myself. I was driven by the tragedy to the verge of accusing my own mind. I suffered the heat of that experience to the extent of adopting the opposite extreme. Sweeping all of that aside, I began by splitting my mind into many compartments: for the judge, the accused, the jury, some honorable figures, and the audience. But this failed to lead me onto a path away from the cacophony of the dilemma.

I narrated this to my friend. He said sagely: "This is the fate of all witnesses of the age." Astonished, I asked him: "Then I am neither the judge, nor the accused?" As if he had expected my question, he answered: "Witnesses like you never hesitate to become both judge and accused." I said to him sharply: "But I was defending the people." At once he solemnly replied: "It is better for you to go back to the witness box – that one, in front of the audience, not facing the jury."

I must confess that, when I took refuge in my friend's village, I wanted to spare myself the bitterness of lingering in that tragic, crime-smelling city. In doing so, I never expected so much congruity between my intuitions and what my friend later suggested to me. It was as if an invisible courier had conveyed to him what was taking place in my internal court of justice.

There is no harm in going back to the original stage of events. There it would be easier for me to realise my deepest feelings. The heat of that tragic experience touched the core of my existence and matured my character. Then the ashes covered my once flourishing national hopes, my hopes that the spirit will bloom in my homeland, and the dawn of peace burst through the darkness.

It was within this paradoxical context that my friend inundated me with pearls of wisdom, and goaded me back to the witness box. He said: "Once again I draw your attention to the fact that your diligence and eagerness to harmonise power and wisdom will lead you to assume more complex roles in the court of the age. Condemnation will be your share, and your star will rise – but under the gallows!"

When I visited my friend, I was carrying nothing, save the notebook in which I wrote the details of my defense, the very same notebook which I carried to the court. I shouted, pointing my finger towards the chief judge, thus insulting the dignity of such a respected legal institution. I proclaimed, in a thundering voice, that the absence of all factual evidence from this foul-playing court turned it into a cesspit of crime. I lifted the documents I had at my disposal so that all could see them. It was obvious that my behaviour had nothing to do with legal professionalism. My friend could always see that faint veil which was blinding me to the truth. Thus he kept trying to push me back to the witness box, undressing me of the barrister's heavy gown, and persuading me not to insert my name amongst the noisy clatter of their swords.

"A platform in front of the people?" I asked. "Yes," he replied confidently. I turned round to see it. I saw nothing, save that lonely desk on the floor of the hall. It was partitioning the audience from those ivory towers, within which the illustrious bald-headed judges sat behind a large semi-circular table. They sat sculpture-like, whispering to one another and cold-bloodedly looking down on everyone in the hall. That was provocative to me. So much so that I forgot even the most elementary principle of the profession, the very fabric of my role in representing the sophisticated standards of a respected standing judiciary. At this climax I shouted again, raising my finger and condemning the complete absence of fairness. My finger pointed this time towards the fleet of flesh occupying the middle position in the ivory tower. I had thus achieved the most grievous possible violation of the core of their alleged legality.

"This man has lied to God, and the only verdict is death!" shouted a harsh, fanatical voice. The noisome stench of what they had contrived the night before. And this very court, representing a mere stage for the industry of tragedy, ran in accordance with that theatrical golden rule!

The last thing I remember was that I posed a question about the meaning of the death announced by the judge, as follows: "Death? Do you mean exile beyond those barriers that block our eyes from seeing further?" I also remember, very vaguely, that my question was followed by a hubbub among the audience. This was then followed by a loud, regular tapping upon the semi-circular table behind which the judges sat. The word "Mahkama" followed, after which, silence prevailed. From within that silence, and all of a sudden, the harsh voice erupted again, with what seemed to be a reply to my question: "Death, death and not exile, you idiot!"

After that I cannot recollect anything, except some remote voices from the corners of the hall: "Viva justice! Viva justice!" Then again the harsh voice: "Mahkama". Exhausted, I leant on the desk, resting my head on its surface. At that moment, I fell into a slumber-like state, and saw myself travelling through a tiny hole in the wall of time. At the end of a long tunnel of light, I met my friend who had died a long time ago. I saw caravans of Sufi mystics travelling through crystals of spiritual light. I felt as though my internal court of justice had been rearranged, or I had discovered a bi-directional path between two worlds.

When I awoke and lifted my head from the desk, I was showered with the broad smiles of the sage, decorating my country with birds singing lovely and lively in its wide blue skies – peace.

Mahkama: court (Arabic).

The Text Committee

Abdallah Bashir-Khairi

The ball of talk is bounced between the three of them over and under the polished, shining surface of the glass table. Sometimes they swap languages. All around lie dossiers: fabricated trials, transcripts of interrogations of persons as yet unborn, denunciations of others who have been as good as dead for decades. This is the office and guardroom of the 'revolution' which they launched, suddenly, in order to accomplish what they call a 'most sacred task': to purify the whole realm of words of all that is not 'gentle and becoming'. It is an ideal office, set up in an ideal township, or so the official representative proclaimed in his inaugural speech.

Eyes roll in sockets, following the ball of talk, directing and possessing it. Today's session is a 'point of departure'. So, slyly skilful silence, manipulations of gestures, turns of heads, all of the subtleties of body language hope to conceal important secretive exchanges and thus to help the ball take short-cuts through a clandestine maze of expressive absence, while leaving it free of any apparent marks of conspiracy. And no wonder, for the three eminent men who are rolling this ball are all legends of craftiness. They are, as that inaugural speech put it more than a decade ago, 'the best of men for the best of weighty tasks'.

Cups of coffee and other refreshments surprise the receding shadow of noon, but still they sit, by their standards, straight, and solicit a place on the table for the new family of glasses now being carried in on silver trays, the gleam of which bewitches the beholders' minds. They are indeed in need of these digestifs, for the breakfast meal was rich and sumptuous, and a heated encounter is just behind them. Only a moment before, the maestro of the tribunal concluded his smart summing-up of the exchange so far. He assigned to himself, long ago, the task of writing the idealising reports refusing permission for any text that fails to restrict itself to the literal precepts of the official dispensation. In today's report, the maestro has outdone himself by utterly demolishing the three elements of time past, present and future. He has deconstructed the machine of time, bolt by bolt, and turned its wheel back to the days of superstition. Oh yes, a true maestro!

Their facial expressions relax with the passing of time and the receding shade. For they have completed the day's task to the utmost perfection.

They are a tribunal of mighty ones, oh yes, true descendents of Sibawayh. So ingenious are they in correcting texts that not even a crow that traverses the township's heavens and cries out 'ka!' can escape the tight net of their grammar. Indeed, any such crow would be forced down to the ground and have his flying suit stripped off and torn to shreds; he'd even be shorn of a parachute, if wearing one. They'd tell him: "It's 'kaw', not 'ka'!"

To these oppressive adepts are due the poll-taxes of speech. Through them alone all texts must pass, and none may be corrected except by their committee.

They thunder that the writer of the play *The Cock of Al-Hajja Bahana* must spell the title differently. And they add, in an insinuating tone: "What do you *really* mean by the cock of Al-Hajja Bahana, anyway? And *who* do you mean, eh?!" Before he answers this question himself, the maestro says haughtily: "Leave the text here with us to correct the linguistic errors with which it is no less than rife. Go and don't come back until we summon you!" This is how the Tribunal Committee for Textual Rectification, known as the Text Committee for short, runs its affairs. And faced with ever increasing numbers of texts, it strains towards 'containing the phenomenon', in the impressive phrase of the brainy maestro, by further extending the reach of its effectively unlimited powers.

The playwrights, writing from living experience, have soon filled the Text Committee's files to overflowing with their scenes. But the fate of the poets is yet more grievous! The newspapers publish only sour and rotten little poems, miserable caterpillars of poems, scrunched up for fear of the tempest.

Some send their writings back to the homeland, from exile. But the Text Committee closes down any publishing houses that even give these writers the time of day. The maestro abhors them as 'lunatics'. He vehemently argues in a television interview that the 'character' who wrote the 'so-called' novel *The Wanderer* draws his ideas from the French Existentialists. "Where is *our* National Cultural Heritage in this audacious text of his? Damn him, the deranged heretic!"

As for the poet who published the two collections *The Rose at Evening* and *Why do the Emigrants not Return?* – the maestro says that his rhymes aren't metrical, that is, not symmetrical like a well-constructed building. And what's more, the maestro adds, his handwriting is very bad!

The next morning, in a frenzied 'sacramental ritual', the Committee burns all texts by members of the Literary Society, closes down that group's cultural centre, and appoints a new editorial board for the group's cultural magazine. The cultural centre is moved to a new site, out of sight (and out of mind), where they can enjoy torturing the magazine to death!

Short excerpts from texts by members of the group are broadcast on state television, accompanied by official warnings like those on packs of cigarettes, followed by the appearance of the Committee's members laughing while they toss, like adept grammarians, the ball of speech between themselves.

> **Eric Ngalle Charles** inspired the creation of Hafan Books in 2003. He was on the way to a poetry conference in Llandudno with Tom when he suggested that they should edit an anthology together. The rest is history... Eric grew up in the small village of Buyea, in Cameroon's English-speaking South West Province. He left Cameroon in 1997, aiming to join relatives in Belgium. But he found himself stranded in Russia, of all places. After three hard years there, he obtained papers to travel to the UK, claimed asylum, and was granted leave to remain. He lived in Cardiff for some years, editing a newsletter for DPIA, giving workshops on poetry and displacement in schools, getting married and becoming a father, playing football for Avenue Hotspurs, Ely, and even being profiled as a poet in the HTV series *Melting Pot*. He spent time studying for a BSc in Business Information Systems at UWIC and working on an autobiographical novel, *Bag of Letters*, which will be amazing when it appears. Now separated from his wife and living in London, Eric has been active with the Exiled Writers Ink group there.

My First Language

Eric Ngalle Charles

Oil and water
Never blend –
One stands up,
One beneath.

"Like a gorilla
And a monkey
Claiming oneness," –
Look closer –
"The monkey is monkey
And the gorilla gorilla."

That's not me.
In captivity I eat banana,
In the wild savagery.

Contained,
Leaving my roots,
I was a goat.
I had three kids.
You – a lion –
Had just one,
Still devouring mine.
I replenish my kind,
You wait your turn.

I trespass,
Being a protectorate,
Not knowing
So many distant borders –
What's the difference?
Not deserving the treatment.
Then I skip,
Learning to jump,
Like doctor Jack Mapanje,

The queue staring at me –
I don't have a face
If that's all I am,
As if my mother abused drugs.

Feeling sorry for me
With vouchers as in child play,
Buying food from Tesco
As the fat lady
Questions my strangeness
And witnesses point a finger.
I thought I was a scarecrow.
So be it.

Clarify intent,
Teach truth in history,
Then they may
Not laugh at me.

Then you ask,
What's my first language?
Ask my granny.
Oh no, the generation's gone,
Still confused
Which language they spoke.
I thought
I am Portuguese,
Never owning a plantation
Of my own,
Then I thought
I am German,
Then I realised
The English kicked
The kingdom out.

They said
I was French –
Oh no, Marie! le bread!

Thanks to the queen –
Queen Victoria that is –
I was given the name
Charles.
Rumours say he was the great.
Maybe I'm a Mormon
Tracking a family tree.

Communism never thrived,
Blaming the heat.

Here in Wales,
Starting with "Bore da",
Still wondering –
A first language?
Studying English,
An adopted tongue,
Through life –
What makes you think?
I know my language,
Existing passively,
As others came
And others left,
Surprised why
I speak in tongues.

Friends

Eric Ngalle Charles

The tale is simple.
What if I had friends,
And my friends had friends,
What if I knew
My friend's friends,
And my friend's friend
Knew my friends?
The land would be full of peace
And crops would grow where planted.
What if my friend's friend
Did not like my friends,
And my friends
Did not like my friend's friend?
It would just be you and me.
Then on tree tops
Woodpeckers will sing
As the elders sit for the day.

What if you 'cleansed' my friends,
And I 'cleansed' your friends,
And it was just the two of us?
Let the rivers tell
The untold sorrow,
The grief of one such land –
Then it will be you and me.

What if on your way down
You meet my friends,
On my way up
I meet your friends,
Like those in the days
Of good old Samaritan,
What will be the tale?

Au Revoir

Eric Ngalle Charles

It was the first
And probably the last time
She missed work
Just to be with me
She did not look in my eyes
When I looked at her
I realised she was crying
But she did not want me
To notice her tears
I had been separated
From my mother
Quite a few times
But there was something
Strange about this separation
Internally I was elated
But seeing one's mother cry
Is never a good sight
You begin to wonder
How bad things really are

When I saw my mother crying
For a moment I thought maybe
Staying at home
Resigning myself to fate
Was the best option
But it would have been madness

She hugged me still avoiding my gaze
Then she took my hands into hers
And slowly but steadily
She gave each of my fingers
A gentle bite
Paying tribute to an
Old village adage
Knotting and sealing the fact that

As I struggle to climb
The thoughts and prayers of
My relatives would be with me
As mine would be with them

I almost burst out in tears
But I was embarking on a journey
Of which I had no concept
The least I could do was cry
Instead the combination
Of joy and sorrow
Within me released itself
Through a very faint smile

My sister her husband
And some friends
Who knew my circumstances
Stood by amazed
By what they thought was
Me being courageous
Not knowing that whatever
Courage I seemed to be showing
Was born out of fear
Fear of the unknown

I was dying with
Apprehension and nostalgia
But most of all
The fear of never being able
To see mother again
Where I was going
Was up to God

Playing With Your White Hair

Eric Ngalle Charles

For Mr Ndanga

First lessons in life –
Playing with your white hair,
With fingers stroking
Like boats breaking
Through the tides
Of the black sea,
Once like the darkness
That forever screened the sky.

Our conversation
Of love and passion,
So to speak,
Like you,
An Omega.
You were a Protestant.
What greater love expressed
From father to son
Than playing with your white hair.

With searching eyes
Like those of a young chimp,
My relative! –
Though I was made of clay.

Behind you I stood,
Tracking those lines
Leading to your first white hair,
A novice,
Searching till you fell asleep.
Begging to sleep,
I tangled your hair,
Forming plaits
Like a barbed-wire fence,
Traps

For when you comb your hair.

A merman,
From a long journey he came.
Dried fish,
Sea weeds,
And a pair of shoes –
Gifts for Christmas.

Never rode an "iron horse".

With blissful heart
You gave us food
From your grape vine.

Memory awakens –
Dearest Dad,
Let me play
With your white hair.

Mr Ndanga is the man who taught me most of the essential skills in life. When I was a young man my mother was involved in a ghastly motor accident – the remote cause of that accident has always been blamed on me. My sister had just been posted as headmistress at a nursery school in Mundemba in Ndian Division. Here she met Mr Ndanga. My sister's baggage consisted of my little sister Queenta, my cousin Collins and myself. Mr Ndanga loved my sister and me and brought us up as his own children even when they went on to have their own two kids, Evenye and Fonta. His love and attention to us remained the same. He taught me maths, how to write and how to be independent – all this he taught me while I searched for his white hairs. He told me stories of great men and even got me interested in the tragedy of King Lear and the demise of Tzar Nicholas II.

To this day I call him father, and he still advises me on most things in life. My stay in Russia put our relationship on hold, and when I first came to Britain I relished the opportunity of writing a letter and chatting on the telephone with him. He is retired now and lives in Tiko, South West Province, married to my sister. He still can't ride a bicycle – an "iron horse". Queenta, Collins and I are all away from home. However, I travelled the furthest. —
ENC, 2004

A Mountain and a Sea

Eric Ngalle Charles

A story from a distance.
They were my only witness,
A mountain and a sea
Whose lips engulfed the green sky,
A lasting kiss,
Washing her waves off-shore,
Leaving behind a boat.

That for my home-coming.

The mountain
Like a giant slate,
With trees keeping vigil
Like relatives awaiting
Their departed children.

Her giant gaze
Looking down at me
Like Yomadene,
The guardian,
The mountain
Where my grandmother
Lived after her death.
A mountain of broken hearts.

That for my home-coming.
A shining mountain
Where sheep grazed,
By which means
My heart rejoiced.

That for my home-coming.

On a wet journey to Llandudno
Washing away pain and longing,

A re-born voice crying
Between a mountain and a sea.

Where voices echoed
Across the town's horizon
And conversation on common things.
Wake me from my slumber
Then this poem
Will be over.

That for my home-coming,

Between a mountain
And a sea.

> **Humberto Gatica** was born and educated in Chile. Before being detained in October 1973 under the Pinochet dictatorship, he was involved in community arts and cultural projects with shantytown dwellers, peasants and forestry workers. Released from prison after ten months in August 1974 he left Chile for Argentina. He came to Swansea with his wife, Gabriela, in October 1975, at the same time as a number of other Chilean refugees, several of whom settled here and later played a key role in the foundation of Swansea Bay Asylum Seekers Support Group, at the end of the 1990s.

In 1981–84 Humberto worked in a community arts project in a coal mine in Mozambique, returning to Swansea because of the civil war. From 1987 until he retired in 2010 he worked as a technician on the Photographic Art BA degree course at Swansea Institute (Swansea Metropoltan University). He has published poetry in various magazines (usually in Spanish) and participated in many photography exhibitions, including shows at the Glynn Vivian Museum in Swansea. He has won international as well as national recognition for his English-language poems in the Japanese haiku tradition.

A selection of Humberto's poems (in Spanish and English) and photographs appeared under the title *The Sand Garden* as the first single-author book published by Hafan Books, in 2009. The first four poems here are from that collection. The others are new poems. The poem 'Cwmdonkin Park' refers to the Monkey Puzzle trees, also known as Chilean Pines, which flourished in that park for more than 100 years until recently. They reminded the Chileans in Swansea of home, and Humberto especially of his native region of Panguipulli, in the territory of the indigenous Huilliche people.

Interrogatory

Humberto Gatica

The cold silence
of the interrogation room

Tied hands

Blindfolded

Somebody smokes
and waits

Doors open and close

The faces of torture
confuse my memories
and eclipse my colours

A telephone
rings for ever
and then ...
nothing

Only the vast night
chaotic
and eternal

Exile

Humberto Gatica

I abandon
my bones
in the uncertainty
of airports
I get lost
in cities
under
the nightmares
of lugubrious
hotels
some nights
somebody dies
in my dreams
in others
I chase my
way back
to the music
of my rains
and my broken
landscapes

The Emigrant

Humberto Gatica

Neither
a castaway
nor a traveller
rather he is
a shattered man
knocking on
illusory doors
spending
his desperate
and obscene
language
secretly
erasing
his nightmares
and who awakes
every morning
surrounded
by labyrinths
and broken
dreams

Those Who Arrived

Humberto Gatica

Those who arrived
almost
unknowingly
like mirages
from a nameless
country
in a city
built of light
to survive
like wounded
reflections
of a landscape
whose air
turns into thunder
and their homeland
into fear
they cross
their mornings
through
the uncertain
density
of the fog
with no
other language
than the chill
of the wind
and the persistent
sound
of the rain

Six Poems

Humberto Gatica

No Man's Land – or:
The long walk to forced exile

London – or:
Waking up in an alien city

Stockwell – or:
How to die in a faraway land

Reunion – or:
To the survivors who dance and dance on the remains of their failures

Return – or:
Going back to a land that never was

Cwmdonkin Park – or:
Running into the sacred scent of our distant tribe

No Man's Land

The cold tenderness
of burning
lies abandoned
in the twisting waiting
of the secret path
to the frontiers

In between chiaroscuros
hang
the early ashes
of a new life

London

Streets open
to a crowd
emerging
from the dawn fog
to speed up
into the mild sway
of the breeze
where
whispering voices
crack
and rebuild
on the unmoving light
of fleeting mirrors

Stockwell

In the stillness
of a dying light
the day hides
in the soft swing
of a tree branch
in whose aura
the voice
of a stateless man
vanishes

Reunion

After
many years
their shadows
still grow
among
machine guns

Defiant
they float
unaware
of the void

Return

The stranger
drags his shadow
around a wall
of rough textures
faded writing
and old slogans

Non stop
the wind shakes
a cobweb
and with it
a dead fly

Cwmdonkin Park

As the light
slides
into the leaves
the wind
shakes us
with the hazy echo
of a gallop
and the dying
tinkle
of a spur

>**Soleïman Adel Guémar** is about the same age as the independent Republic of Algeria. He worked there as a freelance journalist, investigating human rights violations and corruption, from 1991 until 2002, when he claimed political asylum in the UK following threats to his life. The last article he wrote as a resident of Algeria was titled 'Investigations Dangereuses' (*Liberté*, 26 November 2002). He and his wife and children were 'dispersed' to Swansea by the Home Office. By now they all have UK citizenship.

Adel won national poetry prizes in Algeria. His poems and short stories were published in various newspapers and magazines there and in France. Translations have appeared in several previous Hafan collections and in *Modern Poetry in Translation*. A volume titled *State of Emergency* collects most of his poems written in Algeria, in French alongside English translations. It was published in 2007 by Arc Publications (Visible Poets series) with support from English PEN's Writers in Translation programme. In her Afterword, Lisa Appignanesi (then President of English PEN) wrote: "His surly ironies have a fighter's edge, a tough beauty which ropes us in. Britain has inadvertently inherited a political poet of stature, one whose language sings...".

A selection of Adel's stories and parables from Algeria, *Local Therapy*, was published by Hafan Books in 2011. In summer 2012 he was invited to take part in the international Poetry Olympiad in London.

Here we publish some of the poems Adel has written in recent years in Swansea. Translations by Tom Cheesman and John Goodby.

Eyes Closed

Soleïman Adel Guémar

1

And so at last I left
Wounded from head to foot
Dreams all fuddled
But still intact I tell myself intact
Revived by the brilliantly nubile showers

I took my time in the early morning
Sipping a mint tea in the local café
Before catching a flight to the far side of the world
Three hours away from the cemetery-republic
Where I'd spent my life waiting for a miracle

I cast a last glance back
At the electrically-operated gates
Of the new masters' plush residences
Thrown up in haste
As if to guard against the evil eye
And any chance of ghosts of justice waking

2

Odours of the terroir that keep breaking in
Bring back the vertigo of being dangled
From the topmost floor over a city
Deformed but so beautiful still
Over the heads that throng the streets
Lit by the torches of sham celebrations
Over a sea embellished
With small boats all adrift
Over the bars packed with hardened informers
And nightclubs run by colonel torturers
Over the ceaseless aftershocks of a earthquake censored
Hunted down into the narrowest fissures

Of the tectonic plates of my surviving memory
Of the time of dry heaves flooded in blood

3

I swigged out of dubious bottles
I smoked everything forbidden

It's so quiet I'm hearing
The voices of my childhood
Singing in chorus

I sat myself down on the ground
I wiped clean the white marble of the spat-upon tomb
And I fell asleep

4

Your hand seeks me in the night
Timidly it wakes me
And halts at my heart
Lingering there
Clutch and caress both

Your hair it covers my face
I inhale perfume of the ocean
The henna'd Sahara of your passions
The breath of trees of virgin forests
In the spring when they're for being lost in

On your back I trace those flowers
I've yet to give you
And your tender insurrectionary eyes
You've bewitched me with

I broke my watch
Attempting in vain to stop time

Alone

Soleïman Adel Guémar

I always check doors and windows
Two or three times in a row before going to bed
A habit...
And sometimes this goes on all night
– I ought to see a shrink if I was reasonable
But I'm not –

Some men in cagoules
Approach the house
Take over the garden and try to force an entry
A bad habit
Persistent nightmare

Fear of being taken by surprise
And facing the question
Without much knowing why
I'm afraid I admit it
I don't want to say whatever
Held hostage by mad dogs
Uniformed
Or plain clothes

I've read letters stained with the blood
Of torture victims I never knew
Sheets torn from school exercise books
Smuggled out of prison
Bottles thrown into the sea reached me
The cries of innocents inhabit me

I can't now hold a rose
Without pressing against the thorns
Hypnotised I stare
At my blood flowing
My brain empties
I float over countries where violent death is familiar

Today I hear the bangers explode
Terrified
Gangs of youths play at war
Mimicking their big brothers
Gone off to enslave the world
Throw me provocative looks
Block my way – dirty habit –
Throw insults
I don't quite understand – or don't want to –
While my neighbours barricade themselves behind indifference
I walk on under the street lights
The moon comforts me so little
I think of my children walking beside me
In Johannisburg and Alabama
Affronts suffered in exile
Sometimes have the distance of memory
And the colour of gloomy weather

I arrived one summer's day
Death long since upon my skin
Luck being needed
To find a place in the cemetery
The morning's farewells
Were followed by the astonishment of return
And the joy of reunions

Descending into hell
Algiers gripped by an iron hand
Suffocated between two murderous fires

Arriving in London the red double-deckers
And the old phone boxes had something magical
Swansea enchanted
The sorceress songs of the Gower
The friends and the ambiance in brief
Dylan Thomas a light heart kept me here

My wife reproaches me my thoughtlessness
My tragic poems and my useless dreams

– That detached her from me
The head on the shoulders

Around me the world is deaf
The bombs in the distance don't change that at all
The dead are counted in approximations
I read Cioran and Prigogine
And life goes on

Swansea what have you in store for me?

Landmarks

Soleïman Adel Guémar

All his life
He lived it fixed
On the horizon

He's suffering from an overdose
Of light

Is there a cure for that?

Good night!

Maze Brain

Soleïman Adel Guémar

In this blood-streaked brain
Scenes construct themselves
Of farewells, of reunions
Open endings
And journeys
With no end in sight

The maze always
Opens onto the path that leads
To the fairyland lake
Where waterfalls
Start nowhere

In this sick brain
Everything's said to be so lovely
But like a butterfly
It's short-lived

No one will ever really know
If it's ill or not
No doubt it'll only tell
Under torture

Singleton Park

Soleïman Adel Guémar

On a wooden bench
On a green lawn carpet
Stretching to the lake
Of the majestic swans
Songs of water rising from it
And cries of children
I smoke my second cigarette
Savouring it
And think you

The sea's so near
I smell the tang
And its timid waves
Whisper to me speak to me
And I sail far away
Not really knowing
Where this delicious surge
Is going to take me
That came to me one evening
When my rebel heart
Thought it found its love

In Algiers, Tunis or somewhere
Mysterious princess
Stalked by men's stupidity
Her dreams don't leave her

Her steep paths
Go to the horizon

Remember

Soleïman Adel Guémar

I see a sky
The nights of our enduring
Doubts which open
Universal
Onto your tear-
Carpetted eyes
That I drink
Down to the source

I dream of your sky
Fertile and tender
That speaks to me of us
That writes me poems
I shall read
I shall sing
Till the dawn
Your smiles bear

But I know your heart
Will never forgive
The treachery of our elders
And of their gross inheritors

Never mind
I promise you they'll pay
For it

Tell our children
Our story
Tomorrow's
Here so fast
They'll have nowhere
Left to hide
This I swear to you

>**Alhaji Sheku Kamara** came to the UK from west Africa seeking sanctuary from civil wars in Sierra Leone and Liberia. From 2003 he became a key player and later captain of Swansea World Stars football team, and he also developed into an admired writer and performer of 'spoken word' poetry. He was highly commended in the 2011 John Tripp Performance Poetry Competition and is now on the Literature Wales 'Writers in Wales' online database. He is often in demand as a poet at events across South Wales. Alhaji has gained UK citizenship and a degree in Public Service from Swansea Metropolitan University (now University of Wales Trinity St David).

The poems by Alhaji printed here are a small sample of his work. They don't include any of his love poems, or poems about Swansea nightlife or Swansea City Football Club. For a bigger sample, get his book *Peace*, published by Hafan Books in 2009 (extended version coming soon).

Mudera

Alhaji Sheku Kamara

Dedicated to all refugees and asylum seekers in the UK

Yesterday I was woken from my sleep
By bombs and gunfire all over my home town.
I saw people running up and down,
Here and there, left and right, east to west.
I saw some killed, some injured,
And women and young girls raped.

O! the bitter memory of loved ones we have lost
And of forced sex by gunmen who claimed
To defend us,
But killed their own people and forced them
To make love at gunpoint.

Boom! Boom! Po! Po!
The bombs and gunfire continued,
People ran to save their lives.
Some swam like fish
From one part of the river that was poisoned
To the safe part of the river.

But he who forced those fish
To go back where they came from
Is worse than he who poisoned that part of the river.

Red! Red! Red! The whole country is painted red
With human blood.
Hot! Hot! Fire burning people's houses and property,
Very hot fire lit by the hawks,
Like farmers burning the forest to start farming.

The clouds were covered by smoke,
People ran to save their lives.
Some flew like birds from a burning tree to a safe one.

But he who caught a bird
And plucked its wings and sent it
Back to that burning tree
Is a murderer.

And that big strong eagle
Who chased that little peaceful bird from its nest
And left it homeless
Is heartless.

O poor bird flying from east to west
Searching for a tree to pass the night,
Don't worry, no matter how long it rains or snows
The sun must shine again
And dry your wet clothes
And keep your cold body warm.

Then you will be able to thank almighty God
And all the good people
Who helped you through.

I Am Not What You Read Or Heard About Me

Alhaji Sheku Kamara

I wake up this morning
Just to find a bill
In the post
That makes me frown
So I strolled down town
To calm myself down

While strolling
And thinking
Of how to get a meal
And pay the bill
All eyes on me
As if I was going to kill
Or steal
So I took a walk up the hill
To chill

Still all eyes glued on me
Looking at me like a fool
But I stick to the gentleman's rule
And stay cool
Coz I'm not a fool

But hang on a sec
Why me you looking at
Like that
Is it because of my hat?
Or what?
Or is it because I'm an asylum seeker
Or a refugee
Or is it because of all the bad things
You read and heard about me?

A refugee am I?
Yep

But do you know what it means to be one
Or do you really think I want to be one?

I am not a thief
Neither a criminal
Nor a bad man
But to you I'm all these
Probably coz what
You read and heard about me
In the news
Portray me as all these

But let me tell you
I am not what
You read and heard
Or think about me

And to you that
Know how to write
But know not how
To write
The right thing about me
Your hand has caused
Suspicion, division, hatred
And lots of problems
Just like the finger
That pulls the trigger
So before you pick up
Your pen next
To write about me
Think straight and right
So you can write
The right thing about me

And to you that
Talk, talk and talk
Lots and lots
Like a parrot
That ate carrot

Take a walk
And think before
You talk about me again
Because your talking
Has caused pain
Hatred suspicion
And division too

Now let me chill
Up this hill
In order not to think
Too much about the bill
So I won't go mentally ill
I still got to pay
The bill though

I Survived

Alhaji Sheku Kamara

This is my survival story
But first let me tell you this
I could have been a dangerous killer
But I chose life over death

My fingers could have been slick
In pulling the trigger
But I chose to use them
In writing about peace and love instead

I could have been rich
In Operation Pay Yourself
But I chose not to get rich
And hurt others in the process

I could have been king in operating
The killing machine
But I see no sense in killing
My fellow human being

I was trapped in a place
Where I could have easily
Picked up arms and run the place
But I chose to tie up my shoe lace
To escape and seek sanctuary

I could have been a fighter
But I'm a lover not a fighter
I could have been addicted to fighting
But I chose to be addicted to peace and love
And I need no rehab and I'm proud of it

I could have died in that war
But I survived
Yes I survived

I survived Face 1, 2 and 3
I survived Operation No Living Thing
I am not boastful
I am grateful and I am thankful that
I survived that war
I survived J6
I survived Operation No Bush Shaking
I survived Alpha Jet
I survived the Shine Pan
I survived Pa Thinker's Bomb
I survived the tailors' measuring tape and
Design of "short sleeve" and "long sleeve"

My heart goes to all the victims and those who died
In that bloody war
Any time I think of what I went through
I feel lucky I survived
But I still feel sad for all the victims
And all those who couldn't make it alive

But I still do feel nostalgia
I miss home
I miss my friends
Those gone and those still alive
I miss Sunday morning football on the beach
I miss those dusty football pitches
I miss the beat games
I miss playing Palampo vs Marade man
I miss playing boys vs girls down the beach and
I miss supporting our darling Leone Stars

"Operation Pay Yourself" and others mentioned in the lines beginning "Face 1, 2 and 3" are the names of rebel army operations in Sierra Leone in the 1990s and 2000s. Militia men wielding machetes offered civilian victims the choice of "short sleeve or long sleeve": hand or arm amputation. "Palampo vs Marade man" means bachelors vs married men.

Dodgy Handshake

Alhaji Sheku Kamara

Take back your fake smile officer
Do you think that I'm a fool
To think that your fake smile
Will make me think that you are cool?
Don't ask me again how do I do
Do you think that I don't have a clue
Of what you up to?
Why are you trying to shake my hand
When the other day you stopped and searched me
Because I shakes a black person's hand
And to you the hand shake was dodgy
And warrant a stop and search?
And you still want to shake this dodgy hand?
Please don't or else you might just stop and search your self
For a dodgy handshake

>**Showan Khurshid** was born in Kirkuk, in Iraqi Kurdistan, but had to leave because of the various wars waged by the former Iraqi regime. After years on the run he found a refuge in Sweden, which gave him its citizenship, for which he is grateful. He came to Wales to study for a Masters in Political Theory. In 2004 he returned to Iraq but was unable to settle and returned to Wales. He lives with his partner and child near Cardiff and works as an interpreter. Showan wrote in 2003:

These excerpts were written for the first time 18 years ago. For me writing would be meaningless if it were not funny, though I can't be certain I succeed. Satire is a kind of revenge you take on your oppressors, and oppressors – we had a lot of them. My home town, Kirkuk, was made to feel hostile and alien to us Kurds. Now the city has been liberated, and for this thanks to the American, British and Kurdish forces. One might say that since we are approaching another era, one should forget and forgive. Indeed that is necessary, but we should also know how to avoid the repetition of the same agonies.

What happened in Iraq and to the Iraqis was because of Arab nationalism and its over-ambitious plan to build an Arabic superpower, in which ethnic groups like the Kurds, and many others as well, had to either assimilate or disappear. So Saddam was not just an accident: he was the one who was able to be as cruel as it takes to fulfil that plan. And that is why he is still the hero of many Arab nationalists – though hardly in Iraq, because the Iraqis now know, some of them belatedly, what it means to be ruled by Saddam.

When I was a kid, people assumed that anyone who had travelled to Western countries must have learnt important things. Now it is time for me to inspect myself: what I have learnt during my stay in the West? What has changed in me? To tell the truth I still feel the bitterness I felt when I was in Iraq. Yet I feel we have a chance now, because I know there is no need to assume that the wrong is something intrinsic to certain ethnic groups. The wrong is in the political culture and the mentality it creates. A bad political culture can create people like Saddam or Stalin. I also know that liberal democracy can allow diverse people to live together, as long as they wish to do so. This possibility was not there under Arab nationalist rule or even in the Islamic Republic of Iran, where many Kurds and other Iranians are also suffering.

So this is the background of my biography. It is not a biography. My biography is not interesting to me at all, perhaps because I am still not able to laugh at it. But if I ever do write it, it will be about how the years of difficulties turned me into a ghost, which is what I feel I am.   *– SK*

The Theory of Shouting

from the epic drama "The Dream of Power"

Showan Khurshid

(The Cunning Man is learning how to gain power.)

The Masked Man: Yes, that's the most modern theory, the theory of shouting. You haven't heard of it? Shouting theory is based on a game, but one in which no one tells anyone else what the rules are. The important thing is to find out the rules and then play. If you leave others in the dark, you win. But how can you know the rules? – Intuition is the answer. Who has this intuition? – Those who can shout. What I'm telling you now is the greatest of secrets. Listen.

What does shouting mean? – It means either that there is imminent danger, or that a wonderful or important change is about to occur. Just think about when you or other people shout. A child cries as soon as it comes into the world. You shout when you're excited, or shocked, or angry, or when you attack. When an important person is carried in a convoy, sirens go wild, and bodyguards sometimes stick their heads out of car windows to act as extra amplifiers. Their gestures are meant to tell you to give way, but the real message is: "Hey, you, insignificant person! It's time you realised how insignificant you are!"

A child communicates through its cry, doesn't it? – For a child, the only important thing is herself. But children are gradually told: It's not only you that's important. Everyone tells them: I'm important too. Some fathers raise sons, only in order to have someone helpless under their control, to whom they can say how important they are. Thus people inhibit and frustrate one another. There are fathers who dream of pushing their sons into positions of power. But these stupid fathers first of all suppress their sons and their shouting, fearing to become insignificant even in their own sons' eyes. (Although they accept being insignificant in the eyes of significant people outside.) These fathers send their sons to the best schools of politics, psychology and economics, hoping they'll learn. And they do learn, and come back home, and the dictator cuts their throats. So these fathers actually send their sons to the butcher. What they ought to do instead, is prepare a room for them where they can go and shriek.

In fact not all people are so repressed. Some find a place where there's no one to tell them to shut their ugly mouth, and there they train themselves to shout and scream. Now you know this important secret, that's the main thing: find a place where you can shout as much as you want.

You see, if you go to the town square and start shouting: "I allow this! I don't allow that!", then some people will say: Let's stop and see. They will say: Rules are being made, we'd better know about them before we break them and get into trouble. Others will be very grateful to you just for telling them the rules they should follow in their lives. These are people who are burdened with a sense that they are breaking rules, although they don't know what rules they are. So they live in anxiety, expecting someone to grab them by the collar and tell them that the time of judgement has come. They'll follow you immediately, saying to themselves: "This man means what he says. He says what he allows and what he doesn't allow. Now at last we can be sure that no one's going to beat us up for doing wrong. This man's a saint. And all these years we've lived in the hell of uncertainty!"

The only other people who need concern us are those who dare to stand in your way. These should simply be crushed. Shouting is a form of capital, it gives a good dividend. We pit the people who are attracted by the yelling against those who are antagonised by it. It's a purely administrative issue. But the key thing is that we let everyone believe that the essence of the matter is the rules, rather than the shouting. Shouting is the thing that has to be kept secret. No one must know that it's the shouting that really matters. That's the trick.

This is the most advanced theory for gaining power. But also it is well established tradition among our leaders. There was a petty clerk, back in the 1930s, who would yell and scream and swear at anything. Some people came and said: "You shout very well. Why don't you go out to those soldiers, they're doing nothing except eating army rations, go and fix them so they attack." Then they told the soldiers: "A very respectable, intelligent, exceptional person with superior powers is coming to see you." And he went to the soldiers and began shouting and yelling right away. The soldiers thought that something terrible must be about to happen. He told them: "Life will lose its meaning if you don't attack!" They got so distressed about this, even though they didn't know what it meant or what would happen if life lost its meaning, that they attacked right away. And so this man's shouting cost the lives of 55 millions.

Another poor man, a shoemaker's son from Georgia, rather a short man, had no shoes. In the queue for his father's shoes his feet were trampled by the rich. Then he joined the party and his fortunes changed. Now he could begin shouting. So many shouts were com-pressed inside him, he shouted more than anyone. He shouted for the proletariat, and wiped out another 20 million. Such a great character! Only you come close.

A third example: this man lived by the edge of a desert, a good place for shouting. And he yelled and shrieked very well. Now his uncle had moved to the city and acquired some power. He knew the importance of shouting. But he was getting on and his windpipe was feeble and sore. So he fetched his nephew to the city to yell for him. But the nephew yelled for himself, not for his uncle. In fact he disposed of his uncle, and buried him and his cousin in heaven, and never allowed them back. Some say it's technically impossible to bury someone in heaven. So perhaps they're just lost on the way back to earth and they'll return some day.

My examples annoy you? – Good. That's what I want. Let your breast fill with anger, so you'll thunder and roar, so your shrieking voice'll reach the corners of the world. You, the glorious herald of the glorious and everlasting message of our glorious and unified nation to the whole world! . . .

(*At this, the Cunning Man shouts and roars like an aeroplane, wild animals, a siren...*)

from The Bridge of the God Daabhawor: A Vision

Showan Khurshid

It is usually said that human sacrifice is performed for religious reasons. But Billaru, the capital city of the Kiran Empire, located on the river Euphrates, somewhere not far south of the modern city of Baghdad, was different.

Six millennia ago, the wise men here – witnessing how power struggles destroy life, civilisation, even decency, pitting son against father, brother against brother – concluded that nothing mattered more than political stability. They suspected that political rivalry was the problem. They did not know democracy, which manages political rivalry by means of rights and elections. Instead, they thought that they might be able to prevent political rivalry through human sacrifice.

Let me report my vision to you.

[...] Realising that he had victimised innocents in the pursuit of justice, Tinal Tinal cursed all people. He decided that only a very heavy-handed, colossal system that denies all desires and passions and puts fear in every heart can control corrupt human nature. "Remember Hobbes," I was told in my vision. "He wanted no less than a Leviathan."

This was Tinal Tinal's mood when he met some people from Billaru. Although some of them were dissidents and had fled the system to the wilderness, they spoke quite positively about their religion. This raises an interesting question: Why should somebody flee a cruel political system, only to go around promoting the very belief system which underlies the political system which victimised and exiled him? But this happens even now. After all, the belief system of Billaru was presented to the people as good, and they certainly took pride in it. They put the blame for what they found horrible in the system – not the prohibition of love or the practice of human sacrifice, but rather the cheating which was prevalent – on their leaders. To blame the leaders is easier than blaming the system of belief. If you blame the belief, you also lose your people, and even if you flee you will not become a part of a new group, you will remain a foreigner for ever. This is why most people keep their old beliefs.

The dissidents of Bilaru, like all Bilaruians, chanted thousands of times over: "Dary dary Daabhawor daras," meaning: "Great, great is the Greatest Daabhawor." This must have brain-washed them. No wonder they felt overwhelmed by his greatness. The more they chanted, the more they felt overwhelmed. Brain-washed people can even feel very sorry for you, if they know that you're a good person but you don't have the same beliefs as they do. They come and try to convert you. It is like Muslims nowadays whose lives in their own countries become intolerable, mainly thanks to Islam itself, and who try as hard as they can get away to other parts of the world. Once there, they entreat most passionately, preach, and exhort others to convert to Islam.

Tinal Tinal must have been a victim of such confusions, the target of appeals and proselytising campaigns. He converted to the Kiran religion and although nearly everyone told him not to go to Billaru, some did advise him to do so, and he told himself: "Let me go and see with my own eyes."

Once there, he found he was a legendary figure whose fame had reached Billaru decades before. He was assigned to execute some love sacrifices. In the beginning, given his conviction that inducing fear is all-important, he was certain of the justice of the task assigned to him. So he happily chopped off heads, one after another. He did not even mind that these heads belonged to those who were the most innocent, beautiful and lovable. In some sense he did not take such attributions literally. Being a diligent worker, he was assigned more and more heads to chop off. Eventually, the great number of heads he was chopping off alarmed him. But he did not revolt. He asked for temporary leave: some time for contemplation. "Contemplation of what?" the bosses asked themselves. They suspected him of having his own notions of right and wrong.

However, they did allow him temporary leave. Later, when it was time to execute Nebon Terrat, he was recalled and told: "You are given the honour of sending the head of the most beloved, the most beautiful, the most intelligent and the most innocent to the great god Daabhawor."

"Do you mean this literally?" Tinal Tinal asked faintly. "Of course, of course, pious believer and great hero, Tinal Tinal." "How can a human being kill the most innocent?" Tinal Tinal asked himself. "My conscience is already burdened. Do they want to drown my conscience in crime?" However, he said nothing and accepted the task, perhaps because he could not believe that they could possibly be so evil. Or he may have been developing the mentality of professionalism or careerism, where you do what you are told without taking moral responsibility. Possibly he wanted to believe that they were using the term "most innocent" in some different, special sense. Or perhaps Tinal Tinal was losing faith in human beings and was seeing no meaning in anything. Or again, he may have been feeling that he was getting old and should not take too many risks. After all, he enjoyed good facilities and even a few slaves to boot. But there was another thought that went on tormenting him: that he might have been intimidated and cowed. This last idea really upset him. "How can I be reduced to being driven by fear, and why don't they just relieve me from this particular task which I don't like when there are all these jerks out there who envy me and would happily undertake the task?" […]

>**Aimé Kongolo** was born in 1981 in the Democratic Republic of the Congo. He has been living in Swansea since 2002. Aimé's poems – written in French, translated by him with Tom and Sylvie – speak of the horrors of war ('historic irony prolonged / by the rotation of injustice': 'The Fall'), but also of the joys of peace and the personal happiness he has found in Wales. For more, see Aimé's English/French book *Reciprocities / Réciprocités* (Hafan Books, 2009). In recent years Aimé has gained a BA (Hons) in Psychology and Sociology from Swansea Metropolitan University (now University of Wales Trinity St David) and an MSc in Clinical Psychology from Swansea University, as well as much experience in working in the 'care industry'. He is a UK resident and proud father to Freya and husband to Claire.

The Ugliness of Anxieties

Aimé Kongolo

1

after being born — I cried
as I cried
I swam in the sweat of dismays
which smells of fresh
dead human bones

after being born — I crawled
as I crawled
I tended towards standing
standing
I tried to walk
and now I am walking
along a dry path
passing under naked trees
undressing my face of sadness
which is credited with the ugliness of anxieties

2

you've come and are standing
to wipe tears
from some unknown eyes
these tears flowing
like rainforest rain

unable to see your hand in the darkness
in the deep night I touch
and hold onto your arm
leaning my head on your shoulder
waiting for the dawn to come
to see your hand's naked softness

Reciprocities

Aimé Kongolo

as I was entering the fish market
　I asked you to wait for me
　　you waited for me, outside, you waited
　　　then you got tired but you waited for me
　　I didn't want the smell of your scent to be poisoned
　by the atrocious smell of the dead wares on sale in the market
by asking you
　you waited for me, and you waited for me
　　in waiting for me
　　　you got tired, and you got tired
　　in getting tired
　but you waited for me, and you waited for me
still, till
　I had come out again
　　as I came out
　　　you'd seen me, and I'd seen you and on seeing me
　　　　you smiled, and you smiled
　　　　then I smiled, and I smiled
　　　　smiling
　we walked and we walked and walking
　I looked at you, and you looked at me looking at you
you looked at me, then you said
　I love you, and again, I love you, twice
　　you looked at me, and I looked at you looking at me
　　　I kissed you, and you kissed me too
　　　kissing you
　　I looked at you, and you looked at me looking at you
　I'd said I love you
you were smiling, and I was smiling
　smilingly
　　you looked at me, and I looked at you looking at me
　you were happy, I was happy too
and you had said, I love you

Echoes

Aimé Kongolo

onto the roof of anguish
ascends an army mutiny

the fly starvation swarms

bullets and bombs
devour the countryside

through your front door
echoes come as dark characters

I broke into your house
all I saw
your teeth still crying

The Grief of War

Aimé Kongolo

pagaille, confusion et impudique guerre mauvaise,
ô, guerre mauvaise!

shambles, confusion and shameless, vile war
o vile war!
where is my father?
o family of vipers!
where are the innocents?
you took them with no pledges

why are you so senseless?
you who plant them, the innocents, in a garden of death —
why did you make me so wretched?
you've taken them on an eternal journey
without looking back
knowing that each child's life is a search for the father

when will your raging hunger be satisfied?
even the new-borns, you come and take them constantly
accursed be you who call us to that feast —
you killer of innocents

o war, where have you taken them?
you have left me only grief
where did you lead them?
bring them back once more onto this long path
onto the human road along which we carry our sufferings
our tiredness and our hunger each without end

woe to the warriors who ruin our fates
despite the bombardments, the earthquakes
we walked after we had suffered
bring them onto this unsure road where we suffer unwillingly
and where there is jealousy, envy, hatred and despair
despair which makes us unable to live, unable

you who inhibit the innocents in living —
you who inhibit them as they walk on this unsure road —
on this path through a pitiless universe of brutal conflict —
stabs in the back too common, innocent passers-by too easy prey
and all one breathes and all one sees is only pain, grief
and blood upon human blood

et tout ce qu'on respire et qu'on voit n'est que douleur, chagrin
et les sangs humains

Paranoia

Aimé Kongolo

sky gives its horizons
with incessant gleams

rust a man's bravery coarsened
silver the purity of a dove's steps
red the blood shed to defend a homeland
green the hope of a soul deadened

heed the emblems of the realm of darkness
the tragedy of prisms
the prejudice of light

and a citizen plans his departure

>**Norbert Mbu-Mputu** is a writer, journalist and editor, and a former United Nations worker in the Democratic Republic of the Congo (DRC). Living now in Newport (Wales, UK), he founded with friends the registered charity South People's Projects (SoPPro), and he is now the Coordinator of The Community Space Partnership, a community project in Newport. He also managed the project 'Bamonimambo (The Witnesses): Congo and Wales Roots and Routes', sponsored by the Heritage Lottery Fund, focusing on activities around the life of the great explorer of Africa, Henry Morton Stanley, who was born in Denbigh (North Wales).

Norbert has published several books of fiction, poetry and essays, and has contributed to research publications in anthropology and sociology, under the supervision of the late Professor Father Hermann Hochegger, on topics including the dialogue between Africa and other cultures and religions and especially on 'Kindoki' or witchcraft branding and spirit possession. He has often been invited by organizations such as the BBC to give commentaries and analysis on the DRC and on Africa. He formerly worked as a journalist with Radio Elikya, the Catholic radio station of Kinshasa, and published articles in *Renaitre* and *L'Avenir* (Catholic magazines in DRC). He is a correspondent for the USA-based web magazine Congovision.com and the France-based community radio station Mangembo-fm.com. Twice winner of an Unlimited Millennium Award, he founded the company MediaComX Ltd and published the London-based magazine *Congo ya Sika* in English, French and Lingala.

This story comes from a collection Norbert has written, about his life as an exile in the UK, titled: *When the Lion Crossed the River, How I Met Her Majesty the Queen, And Other Stories*. It will be published next year – "inch'Allah!"

"Inch'Allah!"

Norbert Mbu-Mputu

This is not a fairy tale.

From the first days at the Night Shelter, I understood that this asylum life will be a real 'via dolorosa'; a Way of the Cross, with many stations to stand at. But I never believed that I would be so far down, so near to the subhuman condition. Those days also, I started really remembering what my late father always said to me: *"Look: if you are not yet dead, never swear you will be buried with the same head you were born with"*. Anyone who is from our native land must know this proverb. But, this is another long story without end. Let me start this one at the beginning. And it is not a fairy tale.

In fact, everything in our asylum life is about stories; some of them amazing, but most of them tragic and even shocking. Since those first days also I learned one of the big lessons of asylum life in this country: the laughing-cry! It was at Redbridge Night Shelter in Ilford, Greater London, that I learned that lesson.

It was Sarah, a lady originally from Uganda, who told me it, since those first days when I exchanged my London homeless suite for the Night Shelter guest suite. In the Night Shelter, I got another qualification added to being an asylum seeker: I became a 'guest' or a 'client'. I liked it. For the first time I got an identity. I could be identified. I could have a temporary postcode. Because in this country, to live means to have an identity and to have an identity means to have a postcode. And to have a postcode means to have everything else.

That night, when I slept in a proper bed for the first time in two months, when I showered in a proper, normal shower till I dropped, when I ate proper food served by nice, kind volunteers, I understood that my father was right. In this up and down of our life, one needs to dream of eating off a plate, even when using tree leaves as a plate; and the opposite is also true.

That night, as I remember very well, Sarah, the only Black lady guest amongst the six that the Night Shelter could accommodate, came to me, as with my poor English I could not socialise enough with the other guests. I was sitting in the conservatory reading whatever I could find there. She sat down nearby and told me:

My brother (with her pronunciation of her tongue beneath her lips), you are just at the beginning... Those people are not good people. The Home Office is a bad and naughty person. He does not have any heart of flesh; he has bones instead. And he does not pray and believe in God, like you and me.

I could not understand what she wanted to teach me and it took me some time till I understood that she was personifying the Home Office, because I am a very positive person and I like to be on the side of those who take the glass to be half full instead of half empty.

They don't like us... Let me tell you the way to survive in this condition: you need to play comedy; you need to avoid taking everything seriously. You need to play a laughing-cry game, like in Africa when we are mourning dead people: we are crying, and also, at the same time, we use laughing, singing, dancing, joking and eating, even drinking, when we are mourning. This is the only way to survive. Don't waste your time praying the Rosary and the Holy Lady; you will be tired. Don't waste your time imploring God in the mosque or praying five times a day, you will be tired and even God, in such circumstances, seems to remain very far from us... If you are serious like a monk, as I see you now, you will soon become crazy and mad and depressed like me, your sister now... And when they start bombarding you with antidepressants and whatever drugs or tablets, your life will be like mine, your sister, upside down forever!...

I listened to her till a volunteer lady came to sit down nearby; Sarah then disappeared.

When I came back to the Night Shelter one afternoon some time later, I saw it surrounded by police cars and understood that something bad had happened. When we got in, the volunteers told us what had happened: Sarah, my sister from Uganda, my African sister who, for many evenings, had entertained me with her millions of stories, had been arrested and would probably be deported. That afternoon, she had come back to the Night Shelter, shouting, singing and with a bottle of kerosene, and she had spread the liquid over the Shelter door and lit a fire with a match!...

During my nine months as a guest or a client at the Night Shelter, I always thought about her. And I decided to avoid finishing up like her with a mental problem (by the way, I was strongly advised never to use that way of describing anyone), as she had confessed once to me that she had one, because of her long asylum years. One evening, she even came down to the conservatory naked... Even then, we were not allowed to say that she had a mental problem. But anyone could see it…

I decided to become and to remain strong. I decided to start compiling my stories for myself, so that, when I felt depressed, I could start laughing to myself, telling myself my own stories, as I could not communicate enough with my very poor English. Everything in my asylum life became stories and my entire life is now about those stories. And, to be honest, the stories are not fairy tales, even if some of them seem to be fictions…

I became a bag of stories. While others need drugs, cigarettes, beer or marijuana to dream and to forget about the up and down of our lives, I was using my own stories to fly over the moon! And it works. It has helped me since then to keep myself standing, even when sleeping or when the system wanted me to kneel! But, this is another long story with no end.

Let me tell you one of those laughing-cry stories: the day I heard and learned the phrase "inch'Allah!"

Sundays are bad days for the Night Shelter's guests. Most of our places for resting or free meals are normally closed. And even if we are allowed to leave the Shelter a little late, one hour later than the usual 9.30 am, Sunday makes us become nomads more than ever. We only turn around the city centre till evening when we go back in the Shelter.

That Sunday was a very bad Sunday for me. I left the Night Shelter without knowing how I would spend my day. On Sundays the city centre seems closed down; especially the Library, our first place every day when living at the Shelter. When we leave the Shelter, we all pop down to the Library for computing.

I left the Shelter without any special program that Sunday. But also, as the night before we had eaten a nice dinner provided by some volunteer chefs working in a famous hotel, nice food I had not eaten in a long while, I had swallowed it like a mad dog and in the morning I had a real impression that it had opened more spaces in my stomach! I swallowed my breakfast with beans and mushrooms and even added a small left-over cake and also water and juice. But already by 1pm it seemed that I was becoming like a pregnant woman: I was hungry and needed to have some lunch.

In the three months I had spent at the Night Shelter, I always forgot about any lunch during day time. I learned to fill my stomach with my breakfast before leaving and to wait till our supper, back at the Shelter in the evening. That was my routine.

When I left the Shelter that Sunday, I first went to visit one of the Catholic Fathers I knew, not far from the City Centre. Unfortunately, the Father was not there. I then decided to walk to another friend I knew living nearby; unfortunately, he was not there either. *Un malheur ne vient jamais seul* (troubles never come singly), I remembered. Only his wife and children were there. Kindly, the wife invited me to sit and drink water and feel like in my own house, but my priesthood education in the boarding school prevents me from feeling comfortable in such a situation: in a house with a lady, when her husband, even your friend, is not there! In the name of the Father and of the Son and of the Holy Spirit!

I started walking from street to street and from avenue to avenue like a tennis ball. Even the Anglican Church which I knew opened on Sundays was also closed. I could not even pretend to be sitting there, praying, when in fact, for the homeless, open churches are good places to sleep a little, to close one's eyes a little before jumping up for the final blessing. But, this is also another long story.

I was very hungry. I want to put something in my mouth. This had not happened to me for a while during the daytime. My stomach needed something, even a cake or a biscuit. My eyes became greedy and in my brain I started seeing the pictures of a middle-class guy's life I used to see when I was working for the United Nations. I started thinking about my wife and my children, for we had never missed one of our meals. I started smelling my wife's nice dishes, especially when she was cooking my special favourite, crocodile or turtle or elephant trunk, or when she was cooking caterpillars in palm oil sauce. I got tears in my eyes as I started to remember my lovely mother's cassava bread cakes, her soups, or when she cooked special smoked fish mixed with marrow.

I was really so lost in my dreams and my mental pictures that I did not realise I was already in a corner shop, near the petrol station off Ilford Lane. It was not really me, but my feet or my subconscious had brought me there. When I opened my eyes, I started laughing at myself, remembering about Sigmund Freud on my basic psychoanalysis courses at the university. It was my madness which became reality. I was in the shop without really knowing what I wanted. When I looked around, I could see the old bearded shopkeeper in the corner looking at the strange customer who had come into his shop. I did not know how long I had already been there. I needed to act. I had no choice, as he was looking at me, and I was the only customer.

I turned around and saw where the cakes and biscuits were. My eyes crossed from one side to another, while my mind was checking the depth of my pocket. I knew that my pockets, a destitute asylum seeker's pockets, were empty. I was a destitute asylum seeker and I received no support from the government. In fact, 'support' is the polite jargon used by the system. It just means money. They like to make even basic thinking complicated, Sarah told me. But, this is another story, the story of their jargon. You cannot even find a basic *A to Z* for asylum seekers, migrants or exiles...

Those days I could not remember the last time I had seen a pound coin. I remembered my late father and his famous proverb: *"If you are not yet dead..."* How could I imagine my life ending on a London street as an asylum seeker, when months before I had had a house, two cars, a good life, money, a good job and, as usual in Africa, to be honest, all those go together with a nice wife and also some women friends to care about!... Life is a real long story... I remembered Sarah telling me: My brother, my brother, you are still at the beginning of your Way of the Cross!

I did not have a wallet. I checked my four trouser and shirt pockets, and could only feel one small metal coin. When I got it out, it was only 20p. And the smallest cake I could see there was 32p. I looked at the shopkeeper; he kept on looking on me. And I looked at the ceiling: the usual camera or CCTV was there: Smile, you're on camera!

The bad temptation came straight away. I could smell the demon, evil in person, turning around me. He suggested that I could steal the small cake and run away. I am a former football player and that old man has no strength to follow me. I looked at him, I looked at my cake, my cake! and I felt my stomach starting to jump for joy at finding something to put inside it. The temptation became stronger and stronger. It is just a small cake... I will not be killing a human being!

I took the cake and decided to go straight to the shopkeeper. He surely realised that something was wrong with this unusual customer. I came to him with the small cake and made my English even more broken than usual. I asked him how much it cost. He answered quietly that it costs 32p. I showed to him my 20p, but he told me that I need a few more small coins. Which bird could lend me its feathers and wings?... I went back, looked at the 32p cake for the last time and put it down. I wiped away the evil temptation of stealing the 32p cake and running away with it, in the name of Jesus. I smiled at myself, and when I looked at the old man, his eyes were still looking at me.

I started to walk away from the shop. I heard the old man call out me:
Young man, come back, please.
Me, sir? (I became more polite than usual.)
Yes, young man.
I hesitated a little but I was not afraid. I had pushed back the temptation after all. I went to stand in front of his cash register. He said:
Go there, please, and bring me four cakes, the ones you touched a while ago.
I went quickly, even jumping, and came back with the cakes.
Are you a Muslim?
Me?... No sir. I am a Christian; I am a Catholic.
I could see in his eyes that he had mercy on me and he loved me. Giving me the four cakes, he said: It does not matter... Inch'Allah!... Look, every time when you need any cake, just pop down and you will have one. Inch'Allah!
Thank you, sir!
You're welcome.
Every time when I was in a corner, I always popped into the shop just to say hullo to him and when some friends asked me who he was, I said only that he was my Muslim father. As I remember this wise African proverb that says: *"A foreigner is a new friend you did not meet yet. Just open your heart to meet him."*
And this is not a fairy tale!

Part 4

Non-Fiction

Opinion and testimony

I Was Very Lucky

Hans Popper

In the late nineteenth century, the word 'race' became politicized and confused with the word 'nation'. The Jews, so blatantly a mixed community of peoples, were and still are widely – whether naively, or maliciously – called a 'race'.

Before the plebiscite confirming the unification of Germany and Austria in 1938, political slogans were painted on the pavements of Vienna. After Hitler's victory, Nazis hauled Jews out of their flats to scrub the streets clean. Photographs of groups of local people standing around and having a good laugh were, of course, in the press.

As things 'normalised', everybody 'non-Aryan' – i.e. Jewish – could be hauled off the streets or taken from their flats to be interrogated in a police station. Sometimes they were let go again, more frequently put in prison or in a concentration camp. Prison was usually followed by release. In concentration camps, survival was a possibility, but it was rare. Also seized were people known to have belonged to one of the anti-Nazi parties (e.g. the Social Democrats), or anyone else who might be anonymously denounced, usually by the private entrepreneurs – or profiteers and gangsters – who took advantage of confiscated property. If you owned a shop or business, you were well advised to sell it and get away if you could. Some buyers were simply profiteers, but some actually helped their customers.

Acquiring passports and exit visas was not so hard, though it was complicated enough, and was made as unpleasant as possible. Getting entry visas was always the really difficult part. Most if not all countries closed their frontiers to Jewish refugees, only letting in a trickle of small groups. One day it might be fifty to Finland, or twenty somewhere else, for no apparent reason. Special Kindertransports were organized for children, and a few Jews managed to get visas for Palestine (which was then under British mandate). A small number – mostly women – were accepted into domestic service in Britain. Otherwise, you had to be invited by someone who could guarantee for your upkeep. A few people crossed borders illegally, and what happened to them would depend on the grace and favour of the particular country.

Why could so few people get to safety? One reason one always hears is: "The foreigners take our jobs away from us." Yet any economist can tell you that the opposite is the case: immigrants' ideas and initiatives create jobs and other opportunities. The true reasons, in that time of depression and mass unemployment, were stark fear and xenophobia: fear of strangers. An animal smelling an animal from a different herd is put on the defensive. The notorious story of the ship full of refugees sailing from country to country, ending up with all aboard dead, is too well known.

I was very lucky. My mother had English relatives – her uncle had moved to London before the First World War. His wife was the mother of Leslie Howard, the concert pianist, and other artistic boys and girls. Leslie was a big earner, but also a big spender, so they were reasonably comfortable, but not really rich enough to look after us. Still, they helped where they could, and George Howard (a cousin, who was an RAF officer in the First War) worked very hard, even visiting us in Vienna, to help us get British visas. He and a lawyer eventually succeeded in getting us out.

First we stayed in Prague – my father had family there – but the Czechoslovak authorities would not consider extending our transit visa; so on the 27th of September, I think it was, we flew to London. Why did we fly? Because we had to sign an undertaking never to set foot on German soil again (and who could have wanted to?).

When we got out of the plane in Croydon Airport, some official cross-examined us, although everything he could have wanted to know was clear from our passports and visas. How long this might have gone on and what the outcome might have been I can't imagine, but fortunately George Howard turned up, and after a few minutes' conversation, we followed him to his car.

Settling in was a hazardous matter. Work permits were almost impossible to get. We depended on chance amounts of money turning up, often from the overworked refugee organization in Woburn Square.

Eventually I got a free place at a boarding school in the Cotswolds set up by a philanthropic Victorian millionaire. My parents had been asked by the refugee committee to run a house for refugees, and a local clergyman told us about the school. By now the war had started. Soon they were all interned. I was under sixteen, too young to be taken. It was indiscriminate mass internment, no rhyme or reason in it. Most internees were released again after a few months, allegedly on medical grounds. Young men like my older brother went into the forces. Among others, there were a good many suicides . . .

<Hans Popper is emeritus Professor of German at Swansea University. He was born in 1924 and grew up in Vienna. His family fled from the Nazis in 1938 and came to Britain. After army service and qualifying as a teacher, he took a PhD in medieval German and came to work at Swansea University in 1961. Though retired, he is still an active researcher, working on medieval epics and on the philosophy and psychology of emotions in European traditions. He is a volunteer for the Samaritans and writes letters on behalf of Amnesty International.

>Zoulikha Zaidi is an Algerian mathematician. Dr Zaidi came to the UK in 2003 and was granted refugee status in 2005. She spent several years in South Wales before obtaining a post as a Research Associate at King's College London. She is a single mother of three children. At a very young age, she was struck by the unfair and oppressive way women and children were treated, and she realised that religion was used as a powerful tool to make women accept discriminatory social rules. Alongside her work as a university lecturer in Blida, she was involved in an association helping children and youth, in particular child victims of terrorism in her part of Algeria.

Oppression

Zoulikha Zaidi

Those who are lucky enough to live in safer places and more democratic societies don't realise how important it is to feel free to express yourself without the fear of imprisonment or killing, to dress the way you want and not face harassment or assault, to feel safe when walking in the street without the fear of being attacked or killed. Those people just take these valuable and priceless things for granted.

Some people facing oppression give up and let others rule their lives. Others become more rebellious and fight till they get their rights. At the end of their fight, they may feel weaker, but in reality they are stronger.

Fleeing one's home country is never easy. In some societies, when a woman leaves her country, it is already a breach of the 'holy' social rules. She rarely gets support from her own family, regardless how vital it is for her to leave. The rule is, you have committed the crime of being a woman so you should accept, obey, be a minor forever and never argue with any social or religious rules.

For women who are lucky and strong enough to leave oppressive countries, being in Britain is not the end of the journey. Seeking asylum is a long and painful struggle, dehumanizing and depressing. In addition to the pressure of the asylum process itself, there may be problems with language and childcare, and encountering a new culture where they are expected to take charge and make decisions means that they have to continue to be both strong and lucky. Failing to be so with the Home Office will probably lead to disaster.

Most women's asylum cases are not dealt with fairly by the Home Office because it fails to adhere to its own Gender Guidelines, because of negative stereotyping from solicitors, interpreters, caseworkers and/or support workers, or simply because many of the women seeking asylum are not used to taking responsibilities or initiatives.

Being granted Leave to Remain in Britain is not the end of the tunnel. Now you don't have to hide because you are an asylum seeker, but you have to hide because you are not employed. Being a refugee living off the British taxpayer is not something you can be proud of. We come here for safety and freedom but we need dignity, too. We must support ourselves and not feel or appear to be parasites.

Forgiveness

Kimba Cate

Life is difficult in war-affected areas especially for children and women. When I remember what happened to me and my children I can't hold back the tears. All this happened when my husband joined the rebellion to fight the dictatorial regime of Mr Museveni, the president of Uganda. Myself and my children were not aware of my husband's involvement with the rebel activities. We were arrested but managed to escape from captivity and things turned against us. Soldiers attacked our house and searched for my husband and information related to rebel activities.

When they failed to find what they were looking for, they started beating me and my children in order to reveal the whereabouts of my husband and information. Due to the way they treated us that night, we were forced to locate to another part of the country, leaving all our belongings including our beautiful farm. In a way, I will never forget this until my death.

We settled in another part of the country. The second time they attacked our home we didn't know how they came to find us. I think this time they came to kill us because when they broke into the house they told us to remove our clothes and started beating us. The shamba man [*servant*] who was living at the boys' quarters heard the screaming and then the soldiers started chasing him. We decided to run away and in the confusion we managed to escape, scattered in the banana plantation. This time we decided not to live in Uganda anymore.

Things were not so easy as we didn't have the money to pay for the journey. I gave part of our land to a friend who arranged our journey via Rwanda to the UK.

We started looking for my husband using the address which we used to write to him when he arrived here in the UK. When we arrived we were happy because he was not expecting us. It was as if we were dreaming. We cried tears of joy, he begged me to forgive him for what happened to me and the children. We accepted his apology. This happiness was short-lived however as the Home Office refused to allow us to stay with him. He fought tooth and nail but not until the Refugee Arrival Project stepped in to help us could we succeed.

Eventually we were allowed to live together. We had just started building our lives together when a dispersal notice came. We were scared at first and we thought, 'Maybe they are taking us away in Swansea.' Things were not easy until we got to know the Swansea Bay Asylum Seekers Support Group which has changed our lives and we now feel like a part of the community. We are valued here and there is respect for the law, unlike in Uganda. We managed to get an allotment which at least helps to remind us of our life in Uganda.

Even though I now feel like a valued member of the community, I think back to everything I left in Uganda – all the things that took me and my husband time to work for. These are now abandoned and unattended. I can't hold back the tears. I would like to thank Swansea Bay Asylum Seekers Support Group and the community of Swansea. Finally, I request the British Government and other first-world countries to stop financing dictatorial regimes, not just in Uganda but around the whole world.

The Real Garden

Kimba Cate

Me, my husband and our four children,
We took the bus out to Rhossili.
It was scary
But I wanted to see the garden.
A real garden, I was told,
A real garden.

I'm tired of shopping in Tesco.
I want to go back there.
The beans tasted delicious,
The babies slept in the buggy.

A real garden.
It was full of spiders,
Of plants, of flowers.
It reminded me of Africa.

I had wanted to see the garden
And I was happy.

<**Kimba Cate** and her family, from Uganda, lived for several years in Swansea and moved to London in 2010. She told her story to Jeni Williams (for our book *Fragments from the Dark*) and wrote her poem with Sylvie Hoffmann.

>**Latéfa Guémar** was forced to give up her scientific research post in Algeria and flee the country, following attacks on her family as a result of her husband's work as a journalist. Having received refugee status in the UK, she took a Masters in Migration Studies at Swansea University. She has since also undertaken research with the Open University on the reporting of security issues and its impacts on Arabic speakers in the UK, with the Refugee Council on the implications of anti-terrorism legislation for asylum seekers and refugees, and with MIND Cymru on mental health services for asylum seekers and refugees in Wales. She coordinated the 3-year, 11-country project 'Parenting in a Multicultural European City' at Swansea University's Department of Adult Continuing Education. A major outcome of that project was the advice website Swansea-Arrivals.net – still valuable despite no ongoing funding.

Latéfa is currently researching for a doctorate on Algerian women in the diaspora, based at the Centre for Migration Policy Research at Swansea University, and is a Visiting Fellow at the Gender Institute of the London School of Economics. She co-edited *Fragments from the Dark* (Hafan Books, 2008) with Jeni Williams.

Women as Victims of a Rapist State

Latéfa Guémar

Since the beginning of the 'dirty war' in 1992, Algerian women have become the most forgotten victims of the brutal Algerian regime and its national and international accomplices. Women have been targeted both by fundamentalist terrorists and by the police. Like their husbands, brothers and fathers, women have been insulted, beaten and dishonoured by both sides of the conflict.

All kinds of violence against women were organized by the iron hand of the different Algerian state institutions. The systematic practice of rape during the dirty war was officially blamed on the 'terrorists'. But the woman's body was also subjected to campaigns orchestrated by the Algerian regime itself. Brutal sexual abuse became standard.

Studies and reports on the dirty war have been published by international organizations, yet further information about this phenomenon remains limited. No details have been made public about the women violated by soldiers. However, it seems clear that, during the dirty war, rape was a banal act practised by both sides, though the Algerian regime was the most active perpetrator of sexual violence.

Since the start of the conflict, Algerian women have been victims of repression by the various security bodies. Indeed, the 'anti-terrorist fight' was a war against the female population, which was perceived from the very beginning as a tool to be exploited against the enemy.

According to a former army lieutenant now living in exile, in 1993 soldiers were instructed to 'examine' women suspected of being liaison officers in terrorist groups. The instruction was deliberately ambiguous. Suspicions that terrorist Islamists adopted female dress led to deliberately offensive 'inspections'. The Algerian army remains a bastion of male privilege. If they had been serious about examining women appropriately, they would have had to recruit female staff, but this did not happen. The instruction allowed for all women to be considered as potential suspects, and it authorized arrest, examination and the practice of violence against them.

These practices ranged from simple frisking to commands to take off hijabs, to remove skirts or trousers, or even more. Soldiers were allowed to use all forms of humiliation. Certain soldiers also had orders to assess the 'piety' of the women under examination. A shaven pubis was considered proof of a recent sexual act. Shaven hair became a crime committed by women or information for the police to exploit.

As military operations progressed into rural areas, Algerian women were increasingly targeted by the police, more and more often insulted, stopped, questioned, violated, raped and tortured. Certain commanders of operational units ordered soldiers, when visiting places supposedly under 'terrorist' influence, to use all forms of violence against women with the aim of procuring information about their husbands' activities. The objective was to destroy the morale of anyone suspected of belonging to the Islamic side.

As with other forms of torture, the intention was to break and dehumanise these women. Those suspected of hiding political rebels or 'terrorist' husbands could be violated with total impunity: this was an acceptable means of undermining rebellion and 'terrorism'.

Sadly, only a few testimonies and studies about these facts are available to the general public: these women have been betrayed by the shameful silence of all 'enlightened' and 'civilized' agents, by the 'free press', the intellectuals and the political opposition. And because rape is a crime that is a source of shame for many women, victims are often too ashamed to talk about what is nothing less than torture.

The authorized Algerian official press claims that, between 1997 and 2005, more than 2,000 women were kidnapped, violated and, in the majority of the cases, assassinated by terrorists. The true number of women victims, of both sides, must greatly exceed these official figures. Only when a national or international independent organization launches a full enquiry will the truth be revealed.

During the dirty war, revenge and hatred motivated individuals to practise rape against 'terrorist' wives. By declaring a national amnesty, in 2006, the Algerian state established itself as the protector of 'terrorist rapists'. How horrible! How can one remain silent in the face of such acts, where the majority of rapes were authorized and tolerated, even encouraged, by a morally blind and repressive regime?

It is essential today for us, witnesses or victims of these atrocities who have fled and sought asylum in democratic countries, to use the freedom of expression of our host countries to expose, explain and fight – fight for the victims of this form of torture to be recognised and protected under an international convention. Rights can only be attained through struggle: they will never be donated.

My Home

Kera X

My country has a lovely climate. There are months of sunshine, it is open for every visitor. We have a very nice culture of hospitality; we show our love for everyone.

Where I live the town is big and busy. It is the main town of the southern region. There has been a lot of new building in the last ten years but the town was established many years back. I worked in a big hospital there for over thirty years. I worked in every department, in both in-patient and out-patient care. I like to help people.

My house was very big. In my country everyone lives according to their income, of middle class educated people. My house was very modern, everything was fully facilitated. I had a garden and flowers. I had everything I need. I miss all this. I miss my best friends, my family, every love from all those I know.

In general we have a good social life in my country. Nobody lives in his house alone. He will bring some relatives to live with him, or some other people who are not able to live alone. This is the love and experience that we have.

Some people in the country, their children come to the town and learn in the schools to get a good education. They don't mind if they give their children to someone good, so their children have a good schooling. This is how we help each other. Our relatives and our parents, we take them to our houses until they die. No one will be alone in his house. This is another kind of love we have. We don't drop them in one empty house.

In my house I had a girl from a family of my husband's relatives. She stayed with me and helped me in the house, and I helped her continue in her school. She is about fourteen now. When the school was closed she went to her parents to pass the time with them. In school time she stayed with us. Also in my house were my children. One is adopted, my nephew, my brother's son. We adopted him after my brother was killed [by government forces] and his wife escaped. The child is five and a half now. I have not heard about him since I came here.

[*Upset*]

I don't want to say more about this… I don't want to talk about my husband. I want to talk about nice memories.

Our houses are all detached and on one level. We had a good house of mud brick, cemented and painted, with tiled floors, cool to walk on in the heat. The house is painted dark red, and inside a cream colour with white ceilings. It has three bedrooms. It is spacious. Enough for us all.

The area has lots of trees, but I don't have much garden, so I have only four fruit trees. I had flowers on the veranda and growing in the salon. In the salon I grew plants. *Harreg* has big green leaves, climbing up against the wall. *Kaffay abeba* is a small bush I had growing in the garden. It has variegated leaves, green and white, which you may cut and put in the salon. My veranda was full of flowers. I liked to take care of that. I had white roses and pink roses and small yellow roses.

I had many different flowers in the garden. I don't know all their names. You don't buy plants but share seeds and cuttings with friends and relatives. The pergola was covered with a plant growing with small bundles of flowers like grapes. Light purple, very sweet smelling. We liked to sit under the pergola on a long bench, to relax with coffee, in the shade in the hot sun.

We were near by the lake, and all around is small hills. We liked to sit on a veranda and look at all the big trees. Walking for six or seven minutes we came to the lake. There are lots of birds and fish. The birds are yellow, blue on the back, shining blue, golden birds, some big, some small. Many boys go fishing and bring the fish to sell in the town, carrying them in baskets, door to door. Small silver fish. There were many birds on the lake, some we call *daki-ey* have long long legs and neck. There are also some with dark wings and a red pouch under the bill. I have never tried to swim in that lake. There are crocodiles, and there is not a nice beach to sit and relax there. There are long grasses everywhere. We can sit on stones and relax, but we don't go in. For swimming, for the town people, there are two big hotels with pools in the hotel compound, and everyone goes there.

No birds sing at night. Early at six or five in the morning they sing. At seven in the evening it is dark. There is a long summer. In winter it rains sometimes, heavy rain, and then is not very cold. There will be a cloud, you expect rain, it is heavy and then it goes.

[The speaker was anxious after she had finished talking.]

I am thinking about where I say that my brother was killed. Perhaps I will not say this. It is not nice. Perhaps the person who reads it will be upset, perhaps I will say just that he died.

Homelessness

Kera X

To be homeless is very bad. I am just going from house to house. I am completely dependent. I don't have permission to work or to beg on the streets. I don't have money to go to Church. So how can I survive? How can I live going from house to house? And I'm afraid of being detained and deported.

I came to this country to save my life, but I am tortured and depressed here. I really understood how bad it is not to be in my country, so I prefer to go back to my country, and accept all the life-threatening challenges and ill-treatment, even death, among my family and friends.

In my case more weight was given by the Home Office to me speaking English than to my political activities. The Home Office thought, 'How could you speak fluently the language unless you stayed here a long time. You are a liar.' I tried to explain that learning in Ethiopia is in English, from junior to university. We learn our national language as one compulsory subject, but all other subjects are taught in English. But nobody accepts my explanation.

I am sorry to be accounted a liar. I am a nurse, and nursing is an international profession. They could have understood that my English is due to my education. In addition, I was blamed as if I had convinced the physician who diagnosed the damage to my autonomic nerve, after my ill-treatment in detention, so I felt very bad because the physician and I have professional ethics: nurses and physicians could never be solicited by someone. We have Guidance Ethics for all nations. So it was a pity for both of us to be accepted as liars.

Whenever I remember all the happiness I lost from my home and my beautiful country of certainty of sunshine, my tears flow all the time.

All my future is covered by darkness.

<Kera X from Ethiopia prefers to remain anonymous. She told her stories to Jeni Williams.

>Benoit Bizimana Shyalca is a volunteer with Swansea Bay Asylum Seekers Support Group and a trained Parenting Facilitator. His parenting training has been supported by Embrace UK and the Race Equality Foundation, and he has also been trained in Leadership Skills with the African Health Policy Network (London).

Benoit is a Rwandese asylum seeker. He was born in 1968 in Uganda. His parents had fled from Rwanda in 1959 following the revolution by the Hutu majority against the Tutsi monarchy, in which some 150,000 Tutsis were killed. Benoit's father was a Hutu and his mother a Tutsi. They faced threats from both ethnic groups. Benoit and his brother Habimana were educated and worked in Uganda. In 1990, Tutsi rebels in the Rwanda Patriotic Front attacked Rwanda from Uganda, starting a civil war. Benoit did business with the RPF in Uganda. In the 1994 genocide, an estimated 800,000 Tutsis were slaughtered in a few weeks. In 1996 Benoit and his brother were resettled in Rwanda. He started a second-hand clothes business. But in 2001, Tutsi government soldiers killed Benoit's brother and turned against him too, because they had Hutu as well as Tutsi friends. In 2003, following intense threats to his life, Benoit fled the country. He escaped into the Democratic Republic of Congo, and lived there in hiding until 2008, when Tutsi rebels attacked DRC in Goma. Benoit then crossed to Uganda and went on to Tanzania, from where he managed to travel to the UK.

Parents! Look Here!

Benoit Bizimana Shyalca

Domestic violence and abuse is rampant in families and communities throughout the entire world. It starts in homes and spreads to communities and then the entire country. When a country is violent it spreads to neighbouring countries and hence around the whole world. I believe that this is the cause of all these wars in Africa, the Middle East, Asia and indeed in the West, where there is no fighting in home countries, yet the human cost of wars fought in other countries is felt very strongly. It is all due to the failures of families, communities and countries. It all starts with parents.

1. Parenting Through the Life Cycle

As parents we are guardians not only of our families but of our countries and of the world. We need to guide our children so that they will inherit peaceful, healthy, safe communities and countries, a peaceful, healthy, safe world.

There is a cycle of life for every living thing. Parents, communities and countries have the responsibility to support our children and one another through each stage of the cycle. It all starts with parents. Should parents fail, the whole cycle collapses.

During early childhood, parents should make children feel welcome, safe and secure in their homes and communities. Throughout childhood, parents should teach children positive values based on their own ethnic identity, culture, and family and spiritual values. When children learn to understand these values they will be able to respect other people's values and cultures, and there will no longer be the violence we see in communities and countries today.

During late childhood, children must be taught how to care about others and how to behave within the larger community. Parents and communities must prepare them for the responsibilities and privileges of adulthood.

In adulthood, they become the teachers, carers, and nurturers of younger ones. As adults we learn to deny some of our own desires in order to meet the needs of children.

The cycle continues into old age, where we pass on the stories and lessons of our families and cultures with patience, appreciation and acceptance.

These are the four stages. If we can perfect our parenting in all these stages we shall be sure of safe families and communities, and hence a world free of violence.

2. Abuse: Power and Control

Parents must be aware of the problems of violence and abuse in families and communities. Abuse and violence towards children, spouses or partners, and other vulnerable people such as the elderly, sick or disabled, is rampant. It takes many forms – emotional, economic, physical, or sexual – with many motives and contributing factors. Such violence and abuse is always perpetuated through power and control exerted by the abuser. Parents must be vigilant for signs of the abuse of power and control.

Power and control are the abusers' tools. All forms of abuse make the victim feel bad. When the abuser has power and control, he or she threatens and intimidates the victim, creating fear, and then isolates the victim. Then, the power and control is complete and the abuser has achieved success.

3. Equality

Equality prevents abusive power and control. When each person respects, trust and supports others and there is fairness, shared responsibility, openness and accountability within a home, a family, a community, a country – then Equality rules. Conflicts are resolved without threats or violence, but instead through fair negotiation. There is a willingness to accept compromises and to change behaviour – whether it's a person, a family, a community or a country. Decisions are made in partnership. Honesty, respect and responsibility are highly valued.

If Equality ruled, then we would have no domestic and community violence, and no wars among political and military forces. And there would be no asylum seekers and refugees.

Team Roles

Benoit Bizimana Shyalca

You are the Co-ordinator. You are seen as mature, confident, a good chair of meetings, able to clarify goals, promote decision-making and delegate effectively. – But you are also seen as manipulative and offloading work onto others.

You are the Resource Investigator. You are seen as enthusiastic, a good communicator, good at exploring opportunities. – But you are also seen as over-optimistic and tending to lose interest once the initial enthusiasm has passed.

You are the Team Worker. You are seen as co-operative, mild and diplomatic. – But you are also seen as indecisive in crunch situations.

You are the Monitoring Evaluator. You are seen as sober, strategic, able to see all the options and make accurate judgments. – But you are also seen as lacking drive and the ability to inspire others.

Nobody is perfect. Your weaknesses are allowable.

The Madness of Language

Anahita Alikhani

English is the most widely spoken language in the world, and is taught in every country. But spoken English is very different from the polite language which is taught in schools. For somebody like myself, encountering the everyday language when we arrive in Britain can be very perplexing. For example, I've discovered there is one word which can be used to express a huge range of feelings as varied as anger, disgust, happinness, joy, astonishement, drunkeness and so on.

An imaginary meeting between a foreign newcomer and a native of Britain can go something like this:

– Where are you from?

– Persia

– Where the ****ing hell is Persia?

– In Asia.

– Oh! ****ing long way from home!

– Oh yes!

– How's the weather there ?

– Warm and nice.

– Oh ! ****ing brilliant! What the **** are you doing here?

– I'm a refugee.

– Oh, ****ing asylum seekers! Pain in the ****!

– Excuse me, do you have a problem? Do you have piles?

– **** ***!!!

– Excuse me, does this word mean yes or no?

– It means move your ****ing **** and go to hell!

I can imagine that in a hundred years or so, as the language evolves, this word might be used even more widely, for example on the news: "This morning Her ****ing Majesty the ****ing Queen opened her ****ing Jubilee Celebrations..."

Interview with a Foreigner

Anahita Alikhani

To find a job in the UK is even harder than getting status as a refugee. A job interview is even tougher than a Home Office interview. In the Home Office, as long as you didn't make up your case, it is not too difficult to answer all the questions. In a job interview, the questions are bizarre and you don't know how you're supposed to answer them.

The main points in a job interview will be: what do you wear, what do you look like, which part of the world do you come from, what is your religion, etcetera. The right answers depend on the person asking the questions. They always smile, trying to show that they are nice people; they try to fool you with their attitude, and with me they always succeed. The smiles mean: you're never going to get this job. If they seem happy, it's a very very bad sign.

This is an imaginary job interview – slightly exaggerated, but based on experience.

I put my bottom on the chair and try very hard to concentrate, remembering my friend's advice: Don't show how clever you are! Answer their questions with questions! Let them think you are stupid! Take a moment after the question before replying! Don't give a straight answer!

First they show their sympathy:

– Do you need anything? Tea, coffee?

– No, thank you.

Then the four of them start taking turns to ask questions:

– Could you tell us about yourself?

– Actually everything is on the CV.

– We didn't see anything about your father and mother. Can you tell us about your ancestry?

– Sorry, I didn't know I'd be expected to introduce you to my ancestors.

– What are your ambitions?

(They always ask this and I don't know what to answer. If I say I have great ambitions, they'll think I'm a trouble-maker. If I tell them about small ambitions, they'll say: Sorry, our firm is a very big firm and we need a person with great ambitions. I stutter, playing for time.)

– Actually, at the moment my great ambition is to find a job.

– Why have you chosen to apply here?

– Same reason as you did.

– What do you have to offer our company?

– What do you want? You have the right to choose. You tell me what I should do for you.

– How long have you been here?

– Three years.

– Excellent. You have excellent English. Were you able to talk English before you came here?

(God I hate this. This is a very bad sign. They are starting to play with me.)

– No. I learned here.

– Oh, then you have time to practise your English.

– Thank you very much.

– Do you like it here? What about the people?

– Of course, I love being here. The people are very nice and friendly.

(Except for the job interviewers, I think to myself.)

– Do you know anything about the history of Wales?

– Yes. A bit. I can't say I'm an expert but I know something.

– Do you know anything about mine problems?

– Sorry, I don't know anything about your problems.

– No, not my problems, I mean mine problems.

– Ah, yes, mines, they explode if you put your foot on them.

– No, no, mines, coalmines.

– Oh, I'm sorry, I couldn't understand your Welsh accent. You mean in the 60s, the mine problems?

– Yes.

– I watched a documentary about that once, that's all I know.

– Do you know how many schools there are in Wales?

– Oh god, no, I don't.

– OK, how many universities?

– Five or four I think, I'm not sure.

– What are you doing at the moment?

– A job interview.

– No, I mean in your spare time.

– Studying English, writing, painting ...

– Why have you chosen this job? You know you have a very strong accent.

– You too!

(He smiles very nicely. I think, oh god, another disaster, I'm not going to get this job. He looks at me very kindly, and asks:)

– Do you really want this job?

– I really love this job. This is my dream.

– Do you want this job? Then answer this question, and I'll give you the job.

– What's the question?

– What was the name of my father's dog?

Britain Through My Eyes *(excerpt)*

Anahita Alikhani

Contrary to what Iranians believe, the British are mostly straightforward, loveable, warm and kindly towards others. They are, or at least seem to be, patient and polite. They like walking and wait patiently in traffic; they give way, they do not quarrel in the street or race cars or cut in front of other drivers or get in a state when they lose their way in town. There is no hurry. I have yet to see anyone hurrying in a bank or shop or hospital. They always seem to have time to queue patiently till it's their turn.

There are many experienced charity workers here who make life easier for us strangers. Their devotion to others regardless of colour or race was very strange to me, coming from a country where we were constantly told that westerners have no time for anyone else, no compassion, forgiveness, kindness, generosity or love. I have found a great deal of affection here!

In Iran you see few elderly people out and about, but here old men and women are everywhere, well groomed, enjoying themselves. In Iran they must be content to stay in with their families. Here the old women especially enjoy chatting to strangers. First thing in the morning, rollers in their hair, they put their heads out of their front doors, like so many geese. "Where do you come from?" "Why did you leave your country?" "Why did you come here?" And so on.

The design of the houses suits this curiosity well: the sitting-room windows look out over the street, so the old women can keep an eye on everyone, till they think they've got to know someone, then they start a conversation, to make sure that person's real and not imagined.

Young people are very keen on drinking and dancing. Many are highly educated, but uninterested in politics or history. They take their freedom for granted; liberty means nothing to them; only we who have spent years in prison know how valuable it is. It rains so much here, people also don't know the value of water, which for us is life itself.

Some young people appear in the street looking very strange. If you look at them they tell you off or swear at you. If they don't want attention, why do they make themselves look so odd, even frightening? This is what freedom means to them. They can't believe that in my country, long hair or short sleeves will get you a night in a police cell, a haircut and most likely lots of bruises – or that in my country, it's a crime to listen to lively music. When I first saw laughing groups of young people in the streets, drinking themselves silly, wearing skimpy clothes, I was very surprised. Life without freedom is black and painful, but too much freedom causes problems for the young.

No night goes by without the television news reporting some murder or abduction. The difference in Iran is that there, the many people who are killed are mostly reporters, writers or thinkers, murdered by the cruel regime. Here, it's mostly inexperienced young people. I have seen young girls lying drunk in the middle of the street in the early hours. Young men drinking quickly start brawling and swearing. On weekend nights they roam the town drunk, looking for a dark corner to relieve themselves. When you walk about town you have to look out for dogs' excrement and vomit on the pavement, pools of urine, and leftover takeaways. The city is frankly hellish. Poor cleaners, I don't know how they cope. These people seem to forget that the city is their home. In general Britain can't be compared with the rest of Europe in terms of cleanliness. The way reporters and filmmakers always show the countries of the East as filthy and derelict – they should look closer to home!

[…]

People seem to love the arts and collecting artworks. Yet there seem to be no important works of art from ancient times. The British Museum holds not one single ancient British brick. Everything in it was brought over from the East by archaeologists, entire civilisations in the basement. Perhaps they were right to steal works of art from countries like mine, which had real talent for creating treasures but whose later generations did not care to preserve their heritage, or else took revenge on hated predecessors – like the famous Buddha destroyed by the Taleban. If only this government and the Queen were as powerful as Queen Victoria and her governments, the statue would still be safe! And Blair would have been consoling the Queen, telling her that Iraq has great ancient walls, statues and vases, as well as gold and diamonds! The museums of Iraq have been looted. We must wait and see if the stolen treasures turn up in Britain and America.

The Queen symbolises British independence. She makes public appearances, pays no taxes, is very rich, lives in a glorious palace, and answers to no one. Sixty million people work to keep her family in luxury. Without the Queen coming to open things or perform various ceremonies, television would have no programmes, no tourists would come, Buckingham Palace would be empty, and Britain would be dependent, God forbid! Since none of her tasks require mental effort, it would be better to choose a queen among the beauty queens, so that beauty would become a facet of independence, which would then be that much pleasanter.

Poor Tony Blair, watched through a magnifying glass: any small mistake and the mass media react with violence. The Prime Minister looks like a ghost these days. Journalists can be very cruel.

People here choose their government, but are rarely interested in their Members of Parliament. But it's important that they have the right to criticize.

People here are given homes and unemployment benefits. In Iran they're thinking of doing this. Here only a few people are homeless, and I don't know why they are. Even the animals here are luckier than animals in my country. There are few stray animals; nobody throws stones at the pigeons or at cats and dogs. The only homeless animals here are slugs – snails without houses. I feel sorry for them because nobody takes any notice of them or asks why they've lost their homes. I have never seen so many slugs in my life. They always appear after rain. Perhaps Mr X, who would very much like to be an Assembly Member and is unhappy because asylum seekers are lodged in furnished homes, should be thinking more about these poor snails without houses – after all they get no support from the UN. But perhaps he doesn't know what the UN is!

The government here respects the people and their rights. In my country nobody has any rights, but here even asylum seekers do. I personally am very grateful to the government and the people here. One can speak to the police with ease, even get to like policemen. Here people's talents are recognised and cherished. In Iran they knock you down and force you to stay at home for most of your life. The privileges here are the gift of a free society, where it isn't criminal to be critical.

<Anahita Alikhani studied and worked as a tutor in Fine Art at Tehran University, Iran. She was detained by the police and tortured in prison after working with foreign television crews covering student demonstrations, and fled to the UK in 2001. While waiting for a decision on her asylum claim in Wales, she not only wrote and often performed the comic monologues published by Hafan Books (in our anthologies beginning with *Between a Mountain and a Sea*, 2003), she also worked for BBC Wales for a while, made a short documentary film about attitudes to asylum seekers in Wales – titled 'Anonymous' – for Valley and Vale Community Arts, and did a lot of voluntary work for Swansea Bay Asylum Seekers Support Group. She left Wales to live in Brighton in 2009.

We kept the 'f-word' in "The Madness of Language" when we first published it. As a result, *Between a Mountain and a Sea* was not approved for use in schools. Maybe this book will be!

>Andre King Gomis was born in Guinea-Bissau 21 years ago and has lived in Swansea since he was four years old. He is studying for a degree in Public Service at University of Wales Trinity St David in Swansea. When he graduates he plans to apply to join the police. He plays football for Mond FC in Clydach. He is writing a series of stories based on his experiences as a volunteer with Caer Las Cymru, a charity supporting homeless people. Here are some short extracts from work in progress.

from **Book for Tim**

Andre King Gomis

My up and downs sitting in the living room of the hostel with stares of gloom coming my way wondering when will normality come my way. Oh yes this is a mixture of all cultures an international melting pot. Some of them having the time of their lives and for others a stepping stone, others they're like fugitives crossing fifteen different states, some are sick mentally or physically.

Tick tock time stops when night comes and after ten pm lights out, then characters flare out. Mr Loud and Mr Snoring flare out in the middle of the night. Mr Loud is hyperactive, he hardly sleeps and Mr Snoring is doing his best to wake people up.

When day comes again we have mass very early in the morning, many half-awake still attend. Order is the name of the day. Residents have to follow certain rules religiously but I hope everyone is grateful. Many of the residents are living complicated lives. Mine I know is in limbo but I hope things get better for all of us. ...

Question: what is a boy of 19 doing in a convent? Ask for shelter and they give you grace. Lately I've been thinking every day that passes equals me getting older and I'm still stuck here. ...

Sun shining everyone merry but not all is well, some people just can't escape from trouble it seems to follow them everywhere even though we pray 'our father' every day and at the end we say 'deliver us from evil' how ironic but never mind. All I can say is be careful of the wind blowing it might make you go round in circles. Maybe I'm down because of the life I live or run out of luck but it's always good to be responsible for our actions. I go on at a steady pace and things are turning for the better. When doors are locked keep on knocking because after every darkness comes the light. ...

>**Angela Jane McLeary** is 34 years old, a British citizen and currently lives in Swansea. She was detained for just over two years under immigration powers, and was recently released from Yarl's Wood Immigration Removal Centre. She has previously worked in Asset Management and Information Technology Solutions, and was a Chocolatier and an entrepreneur. She has been deeply affected by the way the UK immigration system is run and is now an avid supporter of the Swansea Bay Asylum Seekers Support Group, Freedom from Torture and the Poppy Project supporting trafficked women, which is run by the Eaves charity (see **www.eavesforwomen.org**). Angela hopes to study languages in the future.

Fight for Justice and Fairness

Angela Jane McLeary

People who are asylum seekers have come together in this book after facing atrocities in their own countries and seeking safe haven. They are all different, which can only be a beautiful thing. But they almost all get treated just the same: with suspicion.

The first contact that most of them have in the United Kingdom is an immigration officer. Then they often face questioning tantamount to an interrogation. Standard practice is that most individuals who make an asylum application are refused. Not because the Home Office has evidence against them, but just because it is the norm to say 'No'.

Under the "Detained Fast Track" system, complex cases are, astoundingly, considered within a matter of days, without any independent investigations taking place. 90% are refused. Most of these decisions are based simply on the person's country of origin. If the Home Office lists the country as 'safe', the person automatically enters the DFT system. Trafficked women and survivors of torture or of domestic violence are fast-tracked like this. An appointed legal representative gets just one day to interview the client, translate any relevant documents, commission any expert evidence, and present the case. If people appeal against a refusal, they seldom get legal aid. Under the "Detained Non Suspensive Appeal" procedure there is no right of appeal at all, despite the name!

>> *Read up: www.liberty-human-rights.org.uk/human-rights/asylum and the UK Border Agency's documents at: http://ow.ly/nFK4s*

Having been refused, the people are then encouraged to return to their own countries, whether it is safe for them to do so or not. If they fail to do this, and if (as is very often the case) they cannot legally be deported, then they are detained indefinitely. People who have survived being tortured in their own countries are suffering the "Second Torture" of arbitrary indefinite detention in the UK.

>> *www.medicaljustice.org.uk and www.freedomfromtorture.org*

All this is a clear breach of the United Kingdom's obligations under international law, and indeed the Home Office's own guidelines.

These are not the stories you read in the newspapers every day. These are hidden truths kept behind closed doors. The public is shielded from this truth because it runs against the lies peddled by most newspapers.

Government policies towards minority groups amount to a campaign of negative publicity towards immigrants. People seeking sanctuary face a culture of disbelief.

The last few years have been harsh for asylum seekers. The government has severely cut legal aid funding. The number of firms offering legal aid funded work for asylum seekers has almost halved. Individuals with complex cases inevitably fall through the cracks, particularly as evidence often takes time to obtain and needs special expertise, which is expensive.

Some law firms have set up a process to manage asylum cases that works just like a conveyor belt. They deal with cases in record time and move on to the next. Most of these solicitors are underpaid and overworked. On the other hand, the integrity of the work of some immigration lawyers is questionable, to say the least.

The 'savings' on legal aid mean asylum seekers being put up in expensive accommodation – namely detention centres – at the princely sum of approximately £130 a day, even though it would be cheaper to have them in the community at an average cost of around £21 per day. Detention is costing £75 million a year.

>> *www.detentionaction.org.uk (Publications) and the Evaluation of the "Solihull Pilot" at www.asylumaid.org.uk/pages/policy.html*

Voucher support for asylum seekers means a cashless existence: no way to get something as simple as a bus fare. If housed in the community, many suffer poor housing conditions, and they can be sent with little or no notice to a new part of the country, with no information about what support exists for them, if any. Even complex trauma cases or heavily pregnant women are put on buses, packed off somewhere new, with nobody expecting them or knowing anything about their condition.

It is important that there is a growing group of campaigners who are committed to fighting for justice, fairness and balance. Thanks to their campaigning, the detention of children was ruled to be unlawful in 2011. (However, it has still not actually been stopped!) In May 2013, the High Court ruled that detention of victims of torture is also unlawful.

>> *www.freedomfromtorture.org and www.bhattmurphy.co.uk*

So not all is lost. Most people in Britain remain very welcoming and compassionate. It makes you wonder: who elected the parliamentarians who put the system in place?

Next time you have a moment, visit your MP, tell them your concerns about the changes needed in the asylum and immigration system. It is the job of parliamentarians to listen to the concerns of constituents and to scrutinise the government's actions. We all have to ensure that people in need of international protection are not further persecuted when they arrive in the United Kingdom.

Swansea Bay Asylum Seekers Support Group and a variety of local and national organisations help this vulnerable group of individuals. It is important to continue to fight the injustices experienced by asylum seekers, and small victories have been accomplished thus far, but so much more needs to be done in order to make a just society.

Postscript

This book aims to raise awareness, concern and funds for asylum seekers and refugees. You will not find many detailed stories about the dreadful things that make people decide to flee their countries, the dreadful things that happen as they travel in search of safety, or the dreadful things that still happen, even after they reach supposed safety in Europe. It contains snapshots of feeling, memory and opinion, to help readers imagine refugees as people. That's really all that is needed.

"Are you happy with that?" is a phrase used by some officials at interviews, when what they really mean is: "That's enough about that subject – now I'm going to move on to the next thing." Here "happy" does not mean "happy", and a question is not a question.

Many people imagine that refugees come here in search of happiness. No, they just seek safety, sanctuary.

Who is happy with the world of violence that uproots and scatters people in their ten of millions year after year? A world of wars from which Britain often profits, many started by Britain and its allies, or a result of past British and allied policies?

Happy with the way the few tens of thousands of refugees who reach the UK each year are treated?

Happy with hasty Home Office judgments based on faulty evidence and poor logic, with no right to appeal, no legal advice?

Happy with the detention of innocent people, including children?

Happy with violently enforced deportation?

Happy with destitution – the denial of any entitlement to welfare, housing or food – used as a weapon of public policy?

Happy with the government aiming to create a "hostile environment" towards all migrants? (See: ow.ly/ncHUH)

Happy with politicians and journalists using the term "asylum seeker" as though claiming asylum were shameful and wrong, even a crime in itself?

Happy with politicians and journalists steadfastly undermining the human right to protection from persecution and acts of war?

Who's happy with that?

TC, July 2013

Index of Countries

Useful websites

Swansea

Swansea Bay Asylum Seekers Support Group:
swanseabassgroup.org

Swansea City of Sanctuary: **cityofsanctuary.org/swansea**

Share Tawe (*helping local people help destitute asylum seekers*):
sharetawe.org.uk

Wales

Displaced People in Action: **dpia.org.uk**

Wales Migration Partnership: **wsmp.org.uk**

Welsh Refugee Council: **welshrefugeecouncil.org.uk**

UK

Asylum Aid (*legal support*):   **asylumaid.org.uk**

National Coalition of Anti-Deportation Campaigns
(*contact NCADC if someone you know is at risk of deportation*):
ncadc.org.uk

Detention Action: **detentionaction.org.uk**

Freedom from Torture (Medical Foundation):
freedomfromtorture.org

Medical Justice: **medicaljustice.org.uk**

Refugee Council: **refugeecouncil.org.uk**

Refugee Action: **refugee-action.org.uk**

Two recent Hafan Books publications

Fragments: Transcribing the Holocaust – poeticised transcripts of the life stories of Anka Bergman, Terry Farago and Edith Salter: three survivors of Auschwitz concentration camp. As told to Frances Rapport in Cardiff. 2013. ISBN 978-09569473-90
Available at: lulu.com/hafan and on Amazon

Life Stories – materials for Key Stage 2 Oracy classes in the Welsh national curriculum, using short true tales told by refugees in Swansea. 2012. ISBN 978-09569473-52
Free from: lulu.com/hafan   or from: hwb.wales.gov.uk